Mines of the
Lake
District Fells

Mines of the Lake District Fells

BY JOHN ADAMS

DALESMAN

1995

Dalesman Publishing Company

Stable Courtyard, Broughton Hall,
Skipton, North Yorkshire BD23 3AE

Second Edition 1995

First published 1988

A British Library Cataloguing in Publication record
is available for this book

ISBN 0 85206 931 6

'

Printed by Hubbards

CONTENTS

Foreword

Like me perhaps, you are a fell walker who has come across numerous old mines and as a result have wanted to know more. The way in which we probably differ is that I decided to take my interest further by embarking upon a countrywide search for old mining records. Had I known beforehand the time this was to consume or how difficult an exercise it would be, then I would probably never have started. However, on balance, and now that it is all over, I'm glad I did. Perhaps the most rewarding aspect of the whole experience has arisen from coming into contact with a number of other mine enthusiasts whose knowledge and friendliness has been of enormous help.

The number of documents surviving – mostly 19th century or earlier – is really quite amazing; these take the form of landowners' reports, company reports, engineers' reports, plans, maps, newspaper cuttings and so forth. Unfortunately, each type of document tends only to deal with a specific aspect of a mine, so when all the pieces are put together the result is frequently incomplete and often contradictory. Nevertheless, I have striven to include only information known to be accurate or which I believe to contain a high degree of truth. This done, I am well aware that my conclusions will frequently conflict with those of earlier writers on the subject.

Part I of the book offers what I presume to call a crash course in mining together with an overall view of Lake District working. The latter, I hope, serves to create a context within which individual mines may be considered: the former to afford a better understanding of the second – and major – part.

Part II sets out to satisfy your curiosity should you wish to know more about the actual mines. Here will be found most of those within the Lake District National Park individually listed, along with their history, plans and basic geological features, or, at any rate, as much information as I have been able to find.

Finally, a **warning**. I shall have something to say about mine exploration later, but for the time being please note that whilst many mines are quite safe to explore on the surface, some are not, vigilance being essential at all times. Under no circumstances should you attempt entry for many of those mines still internally accessible are in a very dangerous condition. Particular care should be taken when children are present as their natural curiosity could lead them easily into danger.

Acknowledgements

The following people and organisations have allowed me to use their mine plans:

The Trustees of the Lonsdale Estate Trust (plan on page 134 (bottom); source Carlisle Records Office).

Lord Egremont (pages 24 (bottom), 25 (top), 30, 39, 58, 63, 117, 120/1, 122; source Carlisle Records Office).

Sir William Pennington-Ramsden (page 153 (top and bottom); source Carlisle Records Office).

Waugh and Musgrave, Solicitors, Cockermouth (page 51; source Carlisle Records Office).

Mr J. Spedding, Mirehouse, Keswick (page 101; source Mirehouse).

The representatives of the late Mrs M. S. Radcliffe (pages 71, 77, 80, 85; source North Yorkshire County Records Office, Northallerton).

J. D. J. Wildridge and the Northern Mines Research Society (page 49).

R. E. Hewer and the Northern Mines Research Society (pages 48, 93, 108, 110, 118, 141).

I. Tyler and the C.A.T. Mining History Society (page 105).

Health and Safety Executive, Mining Records Office, London (pages 50 (top), 52, 53, 60, 106, 112).

Carrock Fell Mining Company (pages 92, 94 (top, centre and bottom), 95).

North West Water Authority (page 138).

British Geological Survey, Newcastle (pages, 33, 34, 35, 40 (top and bottom), 44, 50 (bottom), 54, 98, 104, 119, 134 (top), 148/9, 152).

British Geological Survey, London (page 89).

Any plans not so credited are of unknown origin, or ones constructed by myself from old maps and reports, etc.

Most of the information has come from archive collections at the Carlisle, Kendal and North Yorkshire Records Offices and the office of the British Geological Survey at Newcastle. The local history collection at Carlisle Library has been the main source of published material, e.g. learned papers, magazine cuttings, rare books etc. – in particular the *Mineral Resources of Great Britain* series published by the Geological Survey.

The books by Postlethwaite, *Mines and Mining in the English Lake District*, and W. T. Shaw, *Mining in the Lake Counties*, have also been of value. The early history of Borrowdale Graphite Mine is taken from the article by George C. Boon in CW2, lxxvi, the *Transactions of the Cumberland and Westmorland Antiquarian and Archaeological Society* (TCWAAS). Other articles in the TCWAAS have also provided valuable facts. Much of the more recent information on Greenside Mine came from an essay by Arnold Lewis, which is kept in Kendal Public Library. The memoirs of the Northern Mines

Research Society (particularly articles by J. D. J. Wildridge and R. E. Hewer) provided many of the results of recent research.

I am grateful for the help given to me by the following: The staff of the Carlisle, Kendal and North Yorkshire Records Offices. The librarians at Carlisle Public Library. Dr D. B. Smith, Dr D. Millward and Mr B. Young of the British Geological Survey office at Newcastle. Mr B. R. Moore, Mr R. Brownrigg and Mr J. R. Peart of the Buttermere and Westmorland Green Slate Company. Mr A. Gaskell and Mr G. J. Middleton of the Carrock Fell Mining Company. Mr P. Blezard of Broughton Minerals, Kirkby Stephen. Alan McFadzean and Dave Blundell of the C.A.T. Mining Society.

I am especially grateful for the considerable help given by the following people. They are (in alphabetical order): Mrs R. H. Adams, my mother; Sue Adams, my wife; Richard Hewer of the Northern Mines Research Society; Ian Tyler of the C.A.T. and Northern Mines Research societies, Dennis Wildridge of the Northern Mines Research Society; Brian Young of the British Geological Survey.

I must also thank Dave Ramshaw, my regular fell walking companion, for being so good-natured on those many occasions when what was supposed to be a fell walk turned out to be a mine inspection.

Additional notes for the second edition

Page 21 (first line) - Small scale work at Force Crag Mine has now ceased.

Page 45 (paragraph one) - New Coledale Mining Ltd. vacated the site in March 1992.

Page 45 (paragraph four with reference to silver-lead vein at Coledale Head) - A 27-yard Elizabethan type coffin level is to be found on the north side of Coledale Beck, hidden deep in the ravine. The analysis could refer to this site rather than that of Force Crag.

Page 47 (paragraph five) - Efforts were directed into the refurbishment of buildings and preparation of ground in and between levels 0 and 1 for the eventual removal of baryte and blende. Unfortunately a collapse in 0 level, problems with flotation chemistry and poor market conditions combined to make the operation non-viable, so proper mining never truly started. Work ceased in 1992.

Page 97 (paragraph two) - The new owners kept Carrock Fell Mines on care and maintenance while awaiting improved market conditions. As these showed no signs of materialising the site was subsequently cleared of all buildings.

Page 134 - Note the diagram refers to Ruthwaite Baryte Mine (page 102) and not Ruthwaite Lodge Mine (page 132).

Page 146 - Referred to is Eric Holland's *Coniston Copper Mines: a Field Guide*, but in 1987 Cicerone published Eric's *Coniston Copper, A History* which is greatly more detailed than the former.

Part I

Nature of the Mineral Deposits

With the exception of the graphite mines and Honister Quarries,* all other Lake District mines have exploited vein deposits containing compounds of one or more of the following: lead, copper, zinc, silver, tungsten, cobalt, nickel, arsenic, antimony, iron, barium and one or two minerals of small-scale specialist application (e.g. umber for pigments). Many other valuable minerals, including native gold, have also been found in these veins, but never in sufficient quantities to make their commercial exploitation viable.

A vein is a sheet-like body filling a fissure in the rock of a particular neighbourhood (the country-rock). For a given vein the period over which mineralisation took place can be determined from isotopic analysis, and is generally found to have occurred within the range of 400 to 150 millions of years ago. The mechanism involved is still not fully understood though a number of generally accepted theories exist to explain its major features. The central element of these theories is the role played by hot aqueous solutions of the chlorides of sodium, potassium and calcium. These solutions may have been of surface origin though it is more probable that they were released during the metamorphosis of sedimentary rocks. Driven by deep seated sources of heat energy, convection caused the fluids to circulate through innumerable fissures contained within vast volumes of rock dissolving out a wide variety of metallic and other compounds. Favourable physical and chemical conditions within certain of these fissures then caused these compounds to be deposited as the minerals we see in veins. The initial stages of this process produced the so-called primary minerals; for example, sulphides such as galena, copper pyrite, blende and iron pyrite. Subsequent reactions between the primary minerals, water and carbon dioxide produced secondary or decomposition products, for example carbonates such as cerussite and malachite. The explanation of tungsten mineralisation is somewhat different but fluid transport remains the essential feature.

* These are special cases and most of Part I does not apply to them. Their discussion is left until Part II.

Veins, therefore, generally contain a complex mixture of different minerals, which for mining purposes may individually be categorised under one of two headings: ore or gangue. Ore minerals are those which have traditionally been mined for their metal content. Gangue minerals are those which are considered commercially worthless or tend to be used in the form they are found. Examples of the latter are quartz, baryte, fluorite and calcite.

If a vein does contain economically attractive minerals – and many do not – it is not necessarily the case that the sought-after material is uniformly distributed throughout the vein's volume. It may be located in regions called ore shoots separated from one another by large barren patches. Sometimes large bodies of a particular mineral in its pure state are found: these are called ribs or bunches depending on their shape.

The process that caused mineralisation in many instances also brought about a profound alteration of the adjacent country-rock. This altered rock is frequently soft or brittle, and after the vein-stuff has been removed, may collapse or peel away in large slabs. Sometimes the alteration can be particularly severe – this was the case in the Roughtongill workings, where most of the walls were composed of a material very similar to china clay. Not surprisingly, Roughtongill Mine was a difficult and dangerous one to work. The miners, as they worked a vein away, sometimes had to place heavy timbers across the cavity to prevent collapse. These timbers, where still present, are generally in very poor condition and may be completely rotten – one of the many features making contemporary mine exploration so hazardous.

An ore-bearing vein is frequently referred to as a lode. Branching from a vein may be numerous strings or veinlets, themselves possibly rich bearers of ore.

Veins frequently do not occur singly. Usually a mining property will contain several which may be more or less parallel to one another. Sometimes a vein will have a very different trend from others in the locality; it is then referred to as a counter, caunter or cross-vein, in some cases a cross-course.

If two veins intersect then the junction is often – though not always – particularly well endowed with ore. Mining companies would often spend a great deal of money in driving exploratory tunnels to such junctions in the hope of reaping substantial reward – a good example of a rich junction being that of the lead and copper veins at Goldscope Mine in the Newlands Valley.

The width of a vein can be very variable along its length ranging from a few inches to many tens of feet. Sometimes the width is indeterminate since the vein can merge into the country-rock gradually, so that where one ends and the other begins is uncertain.

Quite clearly, a vein is not a perfectly plane sheet of mineralisation, but the deviation from plane is not usually so great that one cannot speak of a course and hade. The course of a vein is the direction taken by its line of intersection with the horizontal so one can, for example, speak of a N-S or a NW-SE vein, and so on. The hade is a measure of its deviation from vertical. A vertical vein would have a hade of 0° whereas an inclined one might have a hade of, say, 26° (equivalent to 1 fathom in 2). Fathoms commonly appear in this book since this was a unit of measurement in which miners worked (1 fathom = 6 feet). In the Lake District most veins are nearly vertical or very steeply inclined and thus have a small hade. Within a given hade and course, two vein positions are possible, so to prevent ambiguity one also specifies an underlie: for example, a vein hading to the east is one whose foot is further to the east than any higher point. It should be remembered, however, that course and hade can vary from place to place within a vein and must not be taken as absolute.

Prospecting for Veins

Today, a wide variety of sophisticated techniques, both physical and chemical, can be of great help in locating veins, but these came too late to benefit most of the mines in the Lake District: the early prospector had to rely on more direct methods.

The surface exposure of a vein is known as its outcrop, and all the veins in the Lake District were discovered at outcrop or in depth by cross-cutting. If a vein outcrops on bare rock then it is usually quite easy to locate. Many sulphide bearing veins weather to give a conspicuous rusty brown outcrop or 'gossan'. In some cases where much quartz is present this outcrop may be very noticeable indeed, appearing as a white ribbon. If the outcrop is slightly obscured large concentrations of metallic compounds can give rise to striking differences in vegetation – very evident to a prospector. In many cases, though, the vein is heavily obscured by deep glacial drift. However, as the Lake District contains many streams there is a good chance that a vein may be exposed in the bed or banks of one. If there is no exposure, and the prospector has reason to suspect the presence of a vein, he will have to roll up his sleeves and dig a trench, but if there is a stream in the locality he may be able to divert it and get his trunch dug for him! Trenches excavated by water are known as hushes. Strange grooves can be found on a number of fell sides, many of these being the overgrown remains of old prospecting trenches.

Sometimes a vein is too weak at outcrop to be obvious so that the only chance of locating it is by a cross-cut, this being a horizontal tunnel driven through barren rock to intersect the vein in depth. If one is found, then this trial cross-cut – or simply trial – may become the means of access for future working. A cross-cut may either be driven towards deep ground from the side of a hill, or from the interior of existing works. As mentioned earlier, it is common for a mining property to contain several, frequently parallel, veins and regular cross-cutting, left and right, from already active workings was a routine procedure.

The term cross-cut is not solely confined to prospecting, for it defines any horizontal tunnel not driven on the direct course of a vein. Cross-cuts can be used for drainage, ventilation and haulage. In established workings a vein, at some point, may be broken and shifted by a cross-course. The evidence of this underground is the sudden termination of the vein by a blank wall of rock or disordered ground: this latter is the name given to the mixture of clay and shattered rock commonly filling fault fissures. Cross-cutting must then be used to relocate the vein.

Opening a Mine

Once a promising vein has been found, it may be decided to develop the initial trial workings into a full-scale mining operation. This is an enormously costly and high risk undertaking, for although the vein might contain considerable quantities of the sought-after mineral, there is a greater chance that it will not. To maximise profits the manner of working must be determined with great care under the aegis of a skilled mine manager, or Captain as he used to be called. For example, wherever possible, the vein should be accessed from the surface by horizontal tunnels, called levels, rather than by shafts, the reason being that veins are usually very permeable and much water may flow into the workings. If shafts are used expensive pumping machinery is required, whereas levels allow gravity to do the job. In addition, it is cheaper to haul mined material along a level than to raise it up a shaft. As the mine gets deeper, further levels are needed and this is continued until such are no longer possible: only then should an internal or external shaft be used. To distinguish an access level from an internal level which may have no immediate connection with the outside world, the term adit is often, though not always, used to describe the former.

The first stage in working a mine may be to drive a level on the course of a vein and remove any useful material from above or below it. This process is known as stoping, the cavities produced being termed stopes.

Stoping can be overhand or underhand. In overhand stoping, vein material is removed from above the level, whereas in underhand stoping it is removed by cutting into the floor or sole of the level.

Overhand Stoping

If a stope is small then it is usually quite safe to remove all the vein material and take it out of the mine for further processing, leaving behind an empty cavity. In a large stope rather more caution may be required. If the vein walls are strong it may still be possible to remove most of the vein material, but a few pillars of unmined material have usually to be left for support.

The Bonser Vein at Coniston Copper Mine was almost wholly stoped out leaving a huge gash, not visible from the surface, 1,500 ft deep and as many long.

If the vein walls are unstable, then other techniques can be used. One method is to increase the height of the level from its usual 6 ft or so to about 16 ft. Heavy horizontal timbers are placed half way up, thereby creating two levels, the wooden floored one having intermittent holes in it, thus allowing access to the one below. The miners then cut away the vein-stuff. Material of value is dropped through the holes and removed from the mine, whereas useless materials (deads) is stacked on the wooden floor. As the stope progresses the deads heap higher and higher providing a working platform. The holes, meanwhile develop into wells which are given a stone or timber lining. The appeal of this method is that it is cheap, a minimal amount of deads having to be taken away, and safe, since the deads prevent the vein walls from caving in.

It will be appreciated that these stopes are yet another feature which makes mine exploration so hazardous. The slightest disturbance to these old and thoroughly rotten timbers could result in the fall of hundreds of tons of rock.

An alternative to the use of timber flooring is to drive two levels, one above the other, and to commence the stope from the upper. Holes are cut through the rock floor to communicate with the level below.

Underhand Stoping

The initial attraction of this approach is that little preparatory work is required, but problems can soon be encountered. For example, the stope may fill with water necessitating the use of pumping equipment. In addition, all deads must be removed.

Prior to the mid-16th century and the arrival of German miners in the district, the technique of tunnelling was not available and all mining was achieved by means of underhand stopes on the outcrop. Even the German miners, to some extent, continued to use this method, and Long Work in the Newlands Valley displays a good example of such an openwork.

To facilitate ventilation, drainage and ore movement, levels are frequently interconnected by means of internal shafts. A shaft sunk from the sole of a level is called a winze, and a shaft put up from its roof, a rise. A blind winze, known as a sump, does not penetrate a deeper level.

Breaking Ground

Prior to the early 17th century and the introduction of gunpowder into mining, all rock-breaking was by hand. Anyone who has ever tried chiselling a hole through a brick wall will appreciate the labour involved, and the prospect of having to drive say, a 100 yard tunnel through solid rock hardly bears thinking about. The technique was to drill a hole in the rock using a hammer and an iron bar called a jumper. When sufficiently deep, two feathers were inserted. A feather is an iron bar, 'D' shaped in section and some 6 in long. A wedge called a plug, or stope, was inserted between the flats and struck by a hammer, the resulting stress shattering the surrounding rock. This work was slow and arduous, and accordingly tunnels were made with the smallest possible cross-section — usually coffin-shaped — just large enough for a man to squeeze through. Later on the plug and feather were replaced by gunpowder, but hand boring was still required to make the holes. No further improvements in rock-breaking appeared until the final years of the 19th century when compressed air drills, safety fuse, electrical detonation and dynamite were introduced.

Ventilation

A long level will not have a good flow of fresh air into it, and one way of providing ventilation is to put up a shaft to the surface, thereby allowing natural air currents to circulate. Along the course of a vein may be many such shafts, but if these are not feasible (or not worth the expense as in the case of a long exploratory cross-cut which may come to nothing) then the air will have to be pumped. A modern mine would use electric fans and plastic ducting, but in the 19th century the fan would be driven by a water-wheel or the efforts of a small boy, and the ducting made of wood or zinc sheet. A common pre-20th century method was to use a waterblast which was a wooden box containing specially designed baffles. In this system water was diverted from a stream and fed — in the most turbulent manner possible — down a shaft and into the box. The entrained air was released and directed into ducts, the water escaping from the mine along a convenient level.

The purpose of ventilation is not only to provide breathable air but to clear airborne dust arising from blasting and other rock-breaking operations. There are no problems with flammable gas as in coal mines. In a modern mine the presence of radon would also have to be taken into account; this is a radioactive gas released in very small quantities from natural decay processes in rocks, especially granite. The early miners were, of course, unaware of its presence.

Dressing of Ore

The process of separating gangue from ore (and/or one ore from another) is known as dressing. Hand-dressing is the most simple method and can be used when the ore is found in large chunks. It is unlikely that this method would be used today, but in the days of cheap labour young boys were often employed for the purpose. Usually, however, the ore is finely disseminated throughout the gangue and more elaborate treatment is required. The first step is to crush the material until it is of a uniform particle size; gravity or floation separation then follows. In the former the crushed material is agitated with water and allowed to settle. In most cases the required ore is the heavier component and settles first, so then it is just a matter of separating two layers, though to increase efficiency the operation may have to be repeated several times on the segregated components. All manner of ingenious devices were invented to automate this process but the principle remained constant. Gravity separation, however, is quite ineffective when the vein-stuff contains two or more minerals of similar specific gravity.

Flotation is a much more recent process and first made its appearance in the Lake District around the time of the First World War. This makes use of the differences in surface tension of various minerals (i.e. the ease with which they are wetted by water) after initial pre-treatment by a suitable conditioning agent and is highly effective on a wide variety of mineral mixtures.

Motive Power

A mine requires some means of driving its crushing machinery, pumps and haulage gear, and most of the mines in the area were well-placed in this respect, using streams to drive water-wheels. Some of the latter were enormous; for example, the water-wheel at Barrow Mine in the Newlands Valley was 60 ft in diameter. Sadly, all of these have long since disappeared, though traces of the wheel pits can often still be found. Water-wheels were sometimes erected inside the mine, but generally they were on the surface and connected to the pumps and haulage gear within by means of long rods and linkages.

In a few instances steam engines have been employed, but their use, whenever possible, was avoided because of the high cost of fuel. More recent mining operations have used water turbines, diesel engines and mains electricity as their prime source of energy.

Conditions in the Mines

Mining, by nature, is dangerous enough but prior to the introduction of effective Health and Safety legislation and a more enlightened attitude of employer to employee, conditions were appalling. Poor ventilation resulted in men inhaling large quantities of dust laden with quartz, lead compounds and other highly undesirable constituents. The consequences for many were silicosis and a wide variety of other debilitating illnesses. Miners were often paid in proportion to the quantity of ore they raised and this encouraged great risk-taking. By the time a man was forty his useful life could be over. This tended to be the fate of the full-time man but quite a few of the Lake District miners were agricultural workers employed in the mines during quiet periods on the farm calendar. In their case, the serious effects were delayed.

By the 20th century matters had improved, and have continued to do so.

Financing the Mine

Prior to the middle of the 18th century, mining was generally financed by major figures of the establishment and, to a lesser extent, by local land-owners. Such investment tended to be sporadic and was often unsuccessful as a result of bad management or lack of technical expertise. However, as the industrial revolution got underway, a new monied-class emerged and with it a rapid growth in mining activity. This was the age of unbridled capitalism, dominated by men – often of humble origin – whose sole aim was the acquisition of wealth by any available means. Any opportunity to make money, however unpromising, was hungrily grasped and numerous small mining companies came into being.

A typical sequence of events in the birth of a mining company was this: a group of businessmen – often local – would become interested in a particular mining property, frequently lured by the claims of a mining man who, of course, stood to get the manager's job! A lease of the mineral rights would be obtained, a company formed and shares put on to the public or private market. Accompanying the share application form would be a prospectus painting an outrageously rosy picture of the mine's future. If and when sufficient share capital materialised, mining got underway.

Today, it might be surprising to learn that such disparate bodies as local shopkeepers, doctors and others had got together to open a mine, but in the great age of laissez-faire capitalism such happenings were commonplace. Here, for example, is the composition of the Hay Gill Mining Company (1839):

Edward Channey, spirit merchant; Thomas Harrison, skinner; George Foster, gentleman; Joseph Irving, gentleman; Samuel Carmalt, spirit merchant; James Wright, coach builder; George Elliot, tea dealer; John Appleyard, gentleman; William Walton, gentleman; Joseph Richardson, spirit merchant; Thomas Low, surgeon; John Gibson, surgeon; Ridley Mewse, sadler; John Jackson, gentleman; Joseph Varty, gentleman; Nicholas Maughan, miner; Thomas Hall, miner; John Robinson, skinner; Thomas Maughan, miner; John Woof, inn-keeper.

Even some members of the clergy were not averse to a little secular dabbling and a number are known to have been speculatively active on the Caldbeck Fells during the early 19th century. Presumably all profits went into their church restoration funds.

By the 20th century this type of company was much less prevalent, the investment tending to come from established chemical and metallurgical concerns.

A Brief Overall History of Lake District Mining

Little is known about mining activity within the district for the period prior to the mid-16th century though there is reason to believe that the Romans mined copper at Coniston. Definite documentary evidence exists, however, of mining in the 13th, 14th and 15th centuries, but these are mere shreds. Suffice it to say that these early mines would be little more than scratchings on the vein outcrops.

The skilled, systematic and heavily-capitalised exploitation of the district's reserves first began in the reign of Elizabeth I. A feature of state policy in those days was the encouragement of new industries and mining was no exception. The driving force in this respect was a parson named Thomas Thurland, who held the position of Master of the Hospital of the Savoy in London. In 1561 he became associated with a Johann Steynberg in a royal grant concerning mines. It should be noted that at this time the Germans were the finest miners in the world, having developed many of the techniques still used today.

Steynberg approached the Augsburg firm of David Haug, Hans Langnauer and Company, which had numerous mining interests in Hungary and the Tyrol, and secured its involvement in setting up a mining industry in this country. The Augsburg company sent a partner, one Daniel Hechstetter, to pursue the matter further, and in 1564 Thurland and Hechstetter were granted the right to mine gold, silver, copper and quicksilver in Cumberland, Westmorland, Lancashire and several other locations. In 1565 a proper mining company was formed in which the firm of Haug and Langnauer held eleven shares, English shareholders holding the remaining thirteen, and in 1568 the company was incorporated by charter as 'The Governor and Society for Mines Royal'.

Initial areas of activity were the Newlands Valley and Borrowdale but soon its interests spread to other parts of the Lake District, rewards and incentives being offered to anyone providing information leading to workable deposits of ore. A large smelting works was constructed at Keswick, and although much of the initial work was done by Germans the indigenous population became progressively involved. As a result of the heavy investment there was, for a while, great prosperity all round.

Hechstetter regularly visited this country to watch over the Augsburg company's interests and in 1571 permanently settled, with his family, in Keswick. In October 1574 Haug and Lagnauer became bankrupt and for a while the company's creditors kept its affairs afloat, but in 1578 all investment from Germany ceased.

Hechstetter remained to look after the English shareholders' interests, but up to this time no profits whatsoever had been made and money was urgently required to keep the venture going. Initially this came from borrowing, but very soon a large debt was incurred and it was suggested that the only way out was to lease the company's rights and properties to persons who might make a go of things.

In 1580 a lease was made to a Thomas Smythe who, in a five year period, made good profits, the royalty payments to Mines Royal allowing the latter company to clear many of its debts. Daniel Hechstetter died in 1591 and his sons, Daniel II and Emanuel, took over the management but never again did Mines Royal do any mining on its own account: the sole role of the company now became that of a grantor of leases.

It is of interest to note that the descendents of Hechstetter were quite numerous and included Thomas Tullie, Dean of Carlisle (b. 1656-d. 1726); Daniel Hechstetter, Headmaster of Carlisle Grammar School (b. 1614-d. 1686); and Sir Thomas Rawlinson, a Lord Mayor of London (b. 1647-d. 1708).

The mining activity associated with Mines Royal lasted well into the 17th century but it is said to have ended with the destruction of the works by Parliamentary troops (c. 1650). The Civil War may well have had an effect on mining activity but, if so, it was certainly short lived since records show that a few hundred tons of lead ore per year, between the years 1649 and 1665, were being raised from mines in the Derwent Fells.

The next phase of well-organised mining activity, again in the Derwent Fells, began with the arrival of a skilled and learned man called David Davies. Davies initially acted as manager to mining investor John Bathurst of London who took a 21 year lease in May 1676, but in 1689 Davies leased the area for himself from Prince Charles, Duke of Somerset. Davies vigorously worked a number of mines in the Newlands Valley and at about the same time there seems to have been a general revival of mining within the district. Activity steadily increased until the mid-18th century when things again really started to get under way. The age of the private mining company had now begun.

Up to about 1870 many mining companies were formed with varying degrees of success, but thereafter rapid decline set in as a result of intense foreign competition. Only the most efficient high-tonnage producers managed to survive into the 20th century.

This century has seen sporadic bursts of mining activity, some of it on quite a large scale, but only Greenside Mine stayed the course, closing in

1962 after some 200 years of almost continuous operation. However, apart from some small scale work at Force Crag Mine, all is now quiet.

It is highly unlikely that any significant mining will take place in the forseeable future. There may well be deposits worth working, but the effect on the landscape of anything but the smallest operation would almost certainly be unacceptable to the planning authority or other interested bodies.

Mine Exploration

Surface exploration of mine sites or rummaging through spoil heaps for attractive minerals can be very absorbing and makes a pleasant diversion on a fell walk. The chance of finding really spectacular mineral specimens is rather remote; nevertheless some quite acceptable ones can be found without too much trouble, some sites being, of course, a lot better than others. However, the inclusion of a mine in this book does not imply any automatic right of access to the site and the reader must use his discretion as to whether or not permission should be sought.

Internal exploration of mines is an entirely different proposition and most definitely not for the novice. It does, of course, take place; for like rock-climbing and potholing it offers considerable challenge and excitement. People who do indulge in it are usually those who already have potholing experience; are very well equipped; have a very good knowledge of mining, and know exactly what to expect. These same people tend to be very interested in mine history or geology and many do much valuable work in this respect. One of the big problems with mines is the hazards can be unseen by all but the trained eye and when disaster strikes it is sudden. It should also be pointed out that most people and organisations having mines on their land forbid unauthorized internal exploration and threaten legal action against offenders.

There is another breed of explorer giving the genuine enthusiast a bad name; that of the professional mineral thief, in it purely for personal gain. Such people are well organised and have in several well-known cases used explosives to break up tonnage quantities of vein material leaving behind an awful mess. The minerals obtained are sold at high profit via various intermediaries to end up in souvenir shops or the like. It should not be assumed that all minerals are obtained in this way, the majority of people in the trade deploring such tactics.

Mine Plans

The way in which mine workings are represented on paper is by means of plans and sections. In a plan, the workings are projected on to a horizontal plane and therefore all sense of depth is lost. In a section the workings are projected on to the vertical plane (or alternatively a plane parallel to that of the vein); thus all sense of perspective is lost. Accordingly, unless one is aware of the means by which plans and sections are produced and the distortions in scale that result, it is easy to get the wrong idea of a mine's layout.

The sole reason for including mine plans in this book is to convey an idea of the extent of the workings and to enable the reader to relate what he sees on the surface to what is underground, but it should not be assumed that each is an accurate representation of a mine on its last day of working – or at any other time! It is an accepted fact that often the plans were badly surveyed, and many mining companies rarely bothered to keep them up to date.

Grid References

Grid references are to six-figure accuracy, and where a group of workings are close together a single reference locates the cluster. Eight-figure references are used only when it has been necessary to differentiate workings in very close proximity. Mining locations have been determined from site visits, OS maps, geological maps and old plans. Some of these documents are over a hundred years old and, although the workings may have been very evident then, they need not be so today. Many of the level mouths and other excavations are now run over with earth, overgrown, and can be very difficult, sometimes impossible, to find.

Part II

Goldscope Mine

A very old lead and copper mine with workings on the E and W flanks of Scope End (NY 226185). On the E side there is one level only, and above it a number of slit-like openworks. This level, the copper vein adit, dates back to 1564 but the openworks could be older by several hundred years. On the W side of Scope End are numerous other levels and openworks, some very old, but the majority 19th century. No work has been done here since 1920.

Mining Details

There is one copper vein and three – possibly four – lead veins. The very early workings were on the Goldscope Copper Lode: this courses approximately E-W and hades to the S at about 1 fathom in 2. The filling consisted of copper pyrite, iron pyrite, and a small quantity of arsenical pyrite in a matrix of smashed country-rock and quartz. The vein is supposed to have yielded some gold but probably no more than the most trifling amount. There is a widespread belief that the mine owes its name to the gold, but this isn't so; the origin of the name is Germanic, not mineral. From the section it will be seen that a large quantity of copper was found at the one place only.

The lead veins course approximately N-S and where they intersect the copper lode displace it a little to the S. From E to W they are met as follows:-

(i) A very small vein about 22 fathoms in from the copper adit portal, but too poor ever to have been worth working.

(ii) The Goldscope Lead Vein, discovered in 1852 when the copper adit was driven forward. The ore-bearing part was of small lateral extent but was extraordinarily rich and, in places, 20 ft wide. The filling was argentiferous galena (7 ozs silver per ton of lead metal) in a matrix of quartz and smashed country-rock. Ore was found in ribs up to 4 ft thick.

(iii) The Sealby vein, named after Isaac Sealby who worked it from the surface in the 1830s. Now here a problem arises: after discovering the Goldscope Lead Vein the miners drove the coppper adit W and discovered another lead vein (marked AA in the diagrams) which they claimed to be Sealby's. However, in 1919, another company of miners declared Sealby's

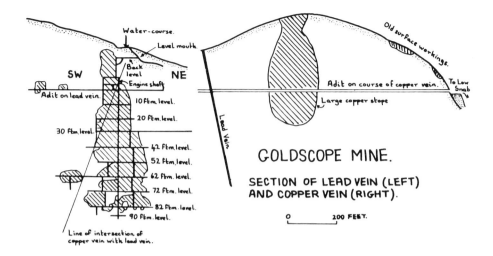

GOLDSCOPE MINE.

SECTION OF LEAD VEIN (LEFT)
AND COPPER VEIN (RIGHT).

0   200 FEET.

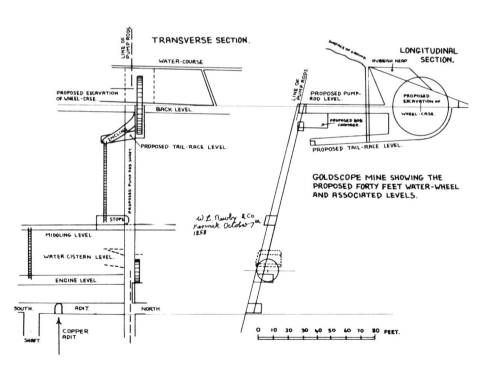

GOLDSCOPE MINE SHOWING THE
PROPOSED FORTY FEET WATER-WHEEL
AND ASSOCIATED LEVELS.

24

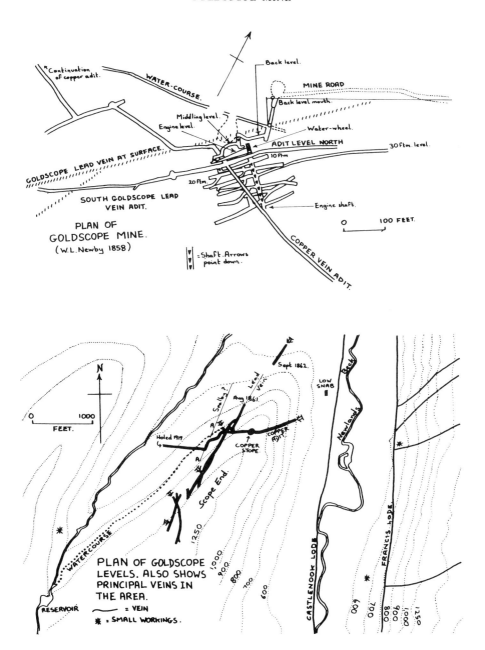

PLAN OF
GOLDSCOPE MINE.
(W.L.Newby 1858)

PLAN OF GOLDSCOPE
LEVELS. ALSO SHOWS
PRINCIPAL VEINS IN
THE AREA.
— = VEIN
✳ = SMALL WORKINGS.

vein to be further W and continued the adit in an abortive attempt to find it. Is then AA the Sealby vein or another?

History

The earliest mention of what may well be Goldscope is found in a 13th century land inventory which tells of a gold, silver, copper and lead mine in the Derwent Fells. If the mine were being wrought at this time, the workings would be little more than surface scratchings on the backs of the veins, for prior to 1564 and the arrival of the German miners, no tunnelling took place. Perhaps the most interesting feature of the referring document is its admission to the possibility of the curious slit workings above the copper adit being 700 or more years old.

The first truly large-scale, skilled and heavily capitalised working of the mine was commenced in 1564 by German miners working for the Company of Mines Royal. The company was evidently very pleased with the mine and spoke of it as 'The best in England', but the attitude of the locals gave much cause for concern. During 1566 the Germans were frequently attacked, and one, a Leonard Stoultz, was murdered. It is not hard to arrive at the reasons for this resentment: the sudden arrival of a prosperous and alien community within the midst of one so poorly endowed gave rise to much jealousy and rancour. Matters could only have been made worse by the fact that the girls of Keswick considered the foreign man to be a good catch, for by 1567 there are known to have been at least fourteen marriages of English girls to German miners, a situation which must have infuriated the local young men. Happily, as a result of the social consequences of intermarriage and a good supply of well-paid jobs these troubles were short-lived.

One person not so easily placated was Thomas Percy, Earl of Northumberland, on whose property Goldscope and several other mines lay. He had not given permission for mining to take place nor did he receive any financial benefit, so quite understandably was incensed and did everything possible to obstruct operations. Inevitably this brought him into conflict with the Crown, the originator of the venture, and in 1568 a trial was held to settle the matter. The judgment went against him and he was instructed to stop all interference. The Earl repudiated the verdict and the ensuing disputes culminated in an armed rebellion and his defeat. He was subsequently executed and his head displayed on one of the gates of York.

It was the German miners who drove the copper adit without the use of explosives and who were largely responsible for the large copper stope shown in the diagram. By 1593 they had sunk 30 fathoms below adit and, around this time, installed an internal water-wheel for the raising of ore and disposal of water. The wheel-driving water was brought by leat along the west flank of the mountain, thence by tunnel into the mine, finally being discharged from the adit.

Within a year of the wheel's installation the mine was abandoned, probably because a more plentiful supply of copper had just been discovered at
Coniston. There are records of some trivial operations in 1611 and 1627, but
effectively nothing further was done until 1649 at the earliest.

It is interesting to learn at this point how this mine acquired its name.
The Germans called it Gottesgab (God's Gift), but local common parlance
gradually distorted it via Gowd Scalp and Gold Scalp to Goldscope.

Sometime in the early 1680s Goldscope was re-opened by one David
Davies. Apart from the absence of the water-wheel, which had long since
been removed, he found the mine in an excellent state of repair and worked
it for both lead and copper. In a letter to Prince Charles, Duke of Somerset,
he mentions the following lead veins:

> First, ye sand vein on Goldscope, lately discovered where there is ore 4 inches
> thick but sore watered. A level might be wrought to clear ye work for twenty
> pounds.
> Second, Little Dale Brow on ye same mountain where we have sunk 12 fathoms
> and have ore constantly, but very hard and not troubled with water, except in
> that very wet season, and then it sinks away in 24 hours. 12 men may be employed
> constantly, and all of them get ore at 50 shillings a ton.
> Third, Tinklers Hole upon the same mountain where I have men at work and ore
> constantly, but hard. We have not made a great trial of it yet.

The sand vein was possibly the Sealby vein, known to be of such composition
(friable quartz), but Tinklers Hole is a mystery. From about 1692 Davies
seems to have shown little interest in Goldscope.

The next event revealed by the records is that in 1697 one Thomas
Robinson, Rector of Ousby, is approaching the Duke of Somerset with
proposals for working the mine. Robinson got his chance but was not a
skilled practical man like Davies: within five years he had made a complete
mess of the enterprise and accrued fairly considerable debts. For the next
hundred years there seems to have been very little, if any, activity at
Goldscope.

In December 1819 a John Tebay of Whitehaven took out a lease on
Brandlehow, Goldscope and other mines, his main interest being in Brandlehow. However on the 3rd August 1835 he entered into an agreement with
Isaac Sealby, a Keswick ironmonger, and James Read, a miner from Loweswater, within which they were granted permission to drive a level below an
existing one known as Lead Work at Goldscope. Pursuant to this, should
the venture prove successful Tebay was to be admitted as a co-partner.
Such conditional agreements were not uncommon, for by sub-letting it was
possible to work a mine without risking one's own capital. Tebay had lost
a substantial amount of money on Brandlehow and doubtless was anxious
to recoup some without further risk. The vein concerned was almost certainly
that later known as the Sealby Vein or lode, but the venture could hardly
be called a success for only 20 tons of lead ore was raised.

On 10th March 1847 the mine was taken by Messrs Clemence, Bowden and Floyd. These gentlemen widened the copper adit – hitherto only the width of a man – and erected a new internal water-wheel and pump for the purpose of working the old copper pocket 40 fathoms or so below adit. They obtained about 50 tons of copper ore but within two years ran out of money and the mine was sold.

In 1849 Goldscope, also Yewthwaite Mine, passed into the hands of Messrs. Clarke, Chapman, Horn and Hart. They drove the copper adit forward from the old workings but never found sufficient ore to cover costs.

One by one the partners left the venture – unable or unwilling to support the mounting losses – and by May 1852 Clarke was on his own. Nevertheless his persistence was rewarded for in September 1852 the Copper Adit reached the Goldscope Lead Vein and the mine was thrust into a period of great prosperity which was to last for twelve years.

A bitter note interposed this success, however, for an ex-partner, Thomas Hart, had unwillingly left the company in May 1850, ousted for being unable to contribute to costs. On his departure he had threatened that if ever the mine became profitable he would fight for the restoration of his position and investment. So in 1853 a protracted legal action was commenced, concluding shortly before Clarke's death. The judgment was in Hart's favour and he regained his share of the mine, this being subsequently purchased from him by Clarke. In 1855, during the course of this trial, the mine's affairs were placed, by the court, in the hands of the celebrated mining engineer, John Taylor junior.

The rich lead deposit, or Great Bunch as it was called, was first worked above adit, but in 1854 a huge collapse – or crush – of unsupported ore wrought such havoc in the workings that the miners were forced to sink below adit. The clearing up of the crush took three years.

At the height of its prosperity the mine employed about 30 persons underground and 20 on the dressing plant. Meanwhile the copper adit was still being driven forward in search of the Sealby Vein, claimed to have been found in 1855, but proving relatively disappointing. The south adit on the Goldscope Lead Vein was also driven forward for a number of years in search of the Goldscope/Sealby intersection, but nothing seems to have come of the project.

Following Clarke's death, the lease was transferred, on Christmas Day 1859, to Messrs George John May and Richard David Holland who, as executors of Clarke's estate, were to run the mine for the benefit of Clarke's children. By this time the workings were 60 fathoms below adit and a 40 ft wheel had been installed to cope with the ever increasing amount of water.

By 1864 the mine was 90 fathoms below adit and all work was stopped. The water-wheel was not sufficiently powerful to cope with water from a greater depth and rather than embark on heavy expenditure the executors considered it in the best interests of the children to close the mine down. In the twelve year period about 5,000 tons of ore was raised yielding 22,000 ozs of silver.

About six years later one H. K. Spark of Darlington took a lease on this and several other mines but seems to have shown little interest in Goldscope. He did, however, drive a trial level of 40 fathoms length into Maiden Hill on the opposite side of the valley. Cross-cuts were driven 6 fathoms N and 6 fathoms S from the forehead but nothing worthwhile was found.

The story closes with W. H. Heywood, a Huddersfield glazing and roofing engineer, who in 1917 invested money in the opening of several old workings in the Newlands Valley and also the Brundholme Mine near Blencathra. Under the direction of Mr Bennett Johns of Keswick, the copper adit was driven further W in the hope of locating Sealby's Vein (see earlier comments on this confusing point), but because of an error in the Newby plan the tunnel came out in daylight 400 yards away from where the miners thought they were! No vein was found, the only reward for their efforts being a meagre 18 tons of ore scraped from the vicinity of the main lead vein. The Spark level was also re-opened and driven on until it struck the Francis Vein whereupon exploratory cross-cuts were made. Again, nothing of value was found.

Yewthwaite Mine

A lead mine situated on the W flank of Cat Bells (NY 240194). There are numerous shallow workings on the back of the vein, but the later deep workings were reached by two levels, the Low Adit at approximately 850 ft A.O.D.* and the Trustees' Level at approximately 700 ft A.O.D. The mine was abandoned in 1893.

Mining Details

There are two veins; the Yewthwaite lead vein on which most of the work was done, and the copper vein, believed to be a continuation of the Goldscope Lode, which was tried but never properly developed.

The Yewthwaite Vein courses 20° W of N and is thought to be part of one large vein of which the Thornthwaite and Barrow lodes are others. It hades to the E at about 1 fathom in 2.3 and the filling was argentiferous galena, cerussite (grey lead ore) and blende in a matrix of quartz, sometimes compact but generally friable. The width was usually 18 in, sometimes as much as 10 ft, but in many places it nipped out completely giving a rather sporadic ore distribution.

The highest working within the site is the Yewthwaite High Adit on Trap Knotts (NY 243189). This is 350 ft long and contains small stopes. There is also a shaft in the floor, about 80 ft in from the entrance.

* Above Ordnance Datum, i.e. above sea level.

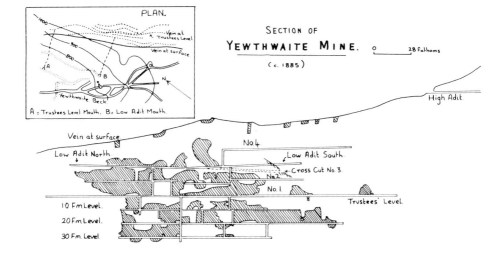

The copper vein (copper pyrite) was tried at Little Mine Crag between Knott End and High Crag (NY 233190).

History

Although most of the Newlands Valley mines are mentioned in very early documents (pre-19th century), Yewthwaite is not. This would suggest it to be relatively young. The earliest available information runs from 1849 when Messrs Clarke, Chapman, Horn and Hart acquired the lease to this and Goldscope mines. They re-opened the Low Adit but failing to find anything of value in the Low Level South, drove the level N and found a good quantity of grey ore. This was processed at dressing floors near the adit mouth, motive power coming from a 16 ft water-wheel.

The mine was worked vigorously right up to the early days of 1853, but following an important lead discovery at Goldscope, Yewthwaite was relatively neglected and most of the hands transferred to the richer mine. In 1854 there were only six men underground, and the year's production a meagre 35 tons of ore.

In 1855, following a legal dispute between two of the partners (see Goldscope for details), the court placed the management of the mine in the hands of John Taylor junior who wished to work it deeper – particularly as the Low Level North was rapidly approaching the surface. The court, however, would not allow any work of a speculative nature so the best to be done was a little stoping in the sole of the level. In the autumn of 1856 all work ceased.

By the latter part of 1859 Andrew Clarke, the only former partner left in the company, had died, and on Christmas Day the mine's affairs passed into the hands of his executors who commenced the driving of a new deep adit level. In 1863 the new adit, or Trustees' Level as it was now called, had reached the vein and was driven S exposing large quantities of ore. The output was approximately 300 tons per year and by 1870 the mine was 30 fathoms below adit. Water and ore were raised by means of a steam engine positioned at the top of the engine shaft, smoke finding its way up through the old stopes and out of the Low Adit.

At about this time the executors ran short of money and sold the mine to Messrs H. K. Spark and B. Plummer. However, the new owners put in little effort and by 1876 – as a result of this and other mining ventures – were bankrupt to the tune of £14,000. For a year or so the trustees for the creditors did a little work in an attempt to recover some of their clients' monies, but nothing came of their efforts and the mine was closed.

Late in 1883 it was taken up by Yewthwaite and Newlands United Mines Ltd, a company formed by one Henry Vercoe, mining engineer from Portinscale, who also had interests in the Barrow and Brandlehow mines. In January 1887 Vercoe had the lease assigned to a calico-printer, Joseph Cunliffe who, according to an old report, was "very much in the hands of Vercoe and his undesirable connections". (Unfortunately this intriguing statement is not clarified.)

The company under Cunliffe retained the same name but did little else and soon the mine was in a poor state of repair. In 1891 an effort was made to explore the copper vein and a level – length 11 fathoms with cross-cuts N and S – was driven for the purpose, but the project was soon abandoned. In an attempt to get the mine working, Cunliffe and his associates tried several times to raise share capital and float a new company. Thus there emerged in 1888 the Mid Cumberland Silver-Lead and Blende Mines Company; in 1891 the Derwentwater Copper, Lead and Zinc Ore Company; and in 1893 the Lakes Mine Company. All these attempts failed.

Castlenook Mine

A small lead mine situated at Castlenook near the southern end of the Newlands Valley (NY 227170). The last work was in 1918.

Mining Details

The major workings lie at the foot of the protuberance and exploited the West Castlenook Lode which runs for over one mile along the valley bottom.

The vein filling was galena in a matrix of smashed rock and a small amount of quartz.

Higher up the hill there are two trial levels (NY 231170, NY 231171). The former is easy to find but the latter is well concealed and lies at the foot of the second waterfall to the N of the first level. Both are fairly short and do not appear to have yielded anything of value.

History

In 1860 the executors of Andrew Clarke, who also worked Yewthwaite and Goldscope, drove an adit level a little above Newlands Beck. This was driven 25 fathoms S on the course of the vein and a shaft sunk 10 fathoms below adit. From the foot of the shaft a level was driven 10 fathoms N and 25 fathoms S and the water pumped out by means of a 16 ft water-wheel. Dressing floors were erected and up to 18 men employed. In 1864, the mine closed. The result of the first three years' work was 55 tons of ore valued at approximately £620.

It is possible that the executors were responsible for one of the high levels but this is not known for sure. In 1917 W. H. Heywood (see Goldscope, Long Work and Brundholme) showed an interest in the high ground and either extended or commenced one or more of the high trials. Within a year he abandoned the project.

Long Work

A small and very old copper mine in the upper reaches of the Newlands Valley (NY 228162).

Mining Details

The Long Work Vein runs approximately E-W and yielded malachite and copper pyrite.

The early workings are Elizabethan in origin and were extended c. 1690. They consist of a line of openworks extending from near the W bank of Newlands Beck to a little beyond the sheepfold. The later works belong to this century and consist of a level very close to the side of the beck and another one in high ground to the W of the sheepfold (NY 225162).

History

The earliest working commenced c. 1565 and later extensions were made by Davies and Robinson (see Goldscope). It appears that little more, if anything, was done until this century.

In 1919 a Mr B. Johns of Keswick working for W. H. Heywood (see Goldscope, Castlenook and Brundholme) drove a level from close to the W side of Newlands Beck to explore the vein 70 ft below the top of the old trench workings. An inclined rise of 31 ft was put up to the bottom of one of the trenches and connection made by a small drainage hole. The Long Work Vein proved disappointing and an 80 ft cross-cut was made to try the southern vein. Heywood was also responsible for the high level but this too was a disappointment. In 1922 he withdrew from all his other mining ventures and Long Work was also abandoned.

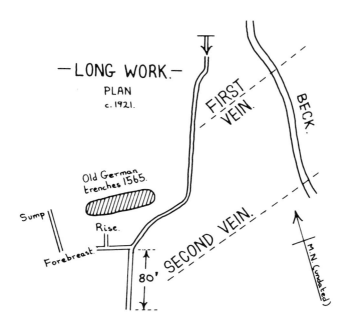

Brandlehow Mine

A lead mine situated on the SW shore of Derwent Water at Brandlehow Bay (NY 250196). Although it was reasonably rich, operations were plagued by a constant influx of water that worsened with depth, reaching a maximum flow of about 150 gallons per minute. As most of the pumping was by steam engine, there being insufficient local water to drive a large wheel, the cost of fuel was a heavy drain on profits. In most mines the water originates at

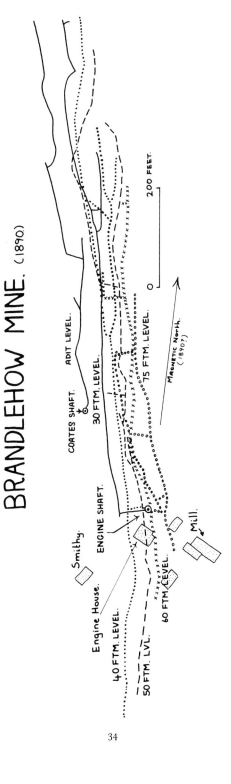

PLAN OF
BRANDLEHOW MINE. (1890)

Smithy.

Engine House.

ENGINE SHAFT.

COATES SHAFT.

ADIT LEVEL.

30 FTM. LEVEL.

40 FTM. LEVEL.

50 FTM. LVL.

60 FTM. LEVEL.

75 FTM. LEVEL.

Mill.

MAGNETIC North.
(1890?)

200 FEET.

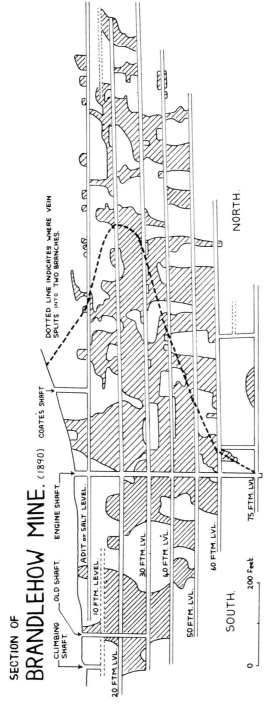

SECTION OF
BRANDLEHOW MINE. (1890)

DOTTED LINE INDICATES WHERE VEIN SPLITS into TWO BRANCHES.

NORTH.

SOUTH.

0   200 Feet.

COATE'S SHAFT

ENGINE SHAFT.

CLIMBING SHAFT.

OLD SHAFT.

ADIT or SALT LEVEL.

10 FTM. LEVEL.

20 FTM. LVL.

30 FTM. LVL.

40 FTM. LVL.

50 FTM. LVL.

60 FTM. LVL.

75 FTM. LVL.

the immediate surface and gains entry through fissures in the rock or via old workings, but Brandlehow was different: some of the water came from subterranean saline springs. An analysis of this water showed a dissolved solids content, weight for weight, of 13 parts per 1,000 sodium chloride (common salt) and 10 parts per 1,000 calcium chloride. Mining ceased in 1891.

Mining Details

The vein worked was the Brandlehow Lode. Near Coate's Shaft this splits into two parts and both cross Skelgill Bank in an approximately NW direction. The northern branch was worked at the Old Brandley Mine and the southern at some ancient pit diggings (see Minersputt). This latter branch is believed to emerge as the Stoneycroft Lode on the W side of the Newlands Valley.

At Brandlehow Mine the vein courses approximately 25° W of N, is 2 ft to 6 ft wide and hades to the E at about 1 fathom in 3. The filling was argentiferous galena (7 ozs silver per ton of lead metal), blende and a little cerussite in a matrix of quartz with a small quantity of baryte. The ore distribution was patchy and whilst in some places it was found in ribs up to 2 ft thick, in many others the vein was poor and barren. A small amount of gold was found but not a·commercially recoverable quantity.

History

This is undoubtedly a very old mine as some of the shallow workings at the N end were cut in pre-gunpowder days, but absence of records precludes an account of this early period.

In 1819 the mine was acquired by a John Tebay of Whitehaven who commenced operations at the S end by driving a westerly cross-cut adit level from the edge of the lake. On intersecting the vein, the level (later known as the Salt Level) was driven N for 100 fathoms and at a number of places ore was discovered and stoped out to surface. A deposit of ore was subsequently found S of the cross-cut and a shaft sunk with levels at 10 and 20 fathoms. Drainage was by means of pumps powered by a 34 ft water-wheel. By 1836 Tebay had lost £2,600 on his mining ventures, mainly attributable to Brandlehow, and shortly afterwards the mine was abandoned.

In 1847 the lease was taken by the Keswick Mining Company (Messrs Langton, Richardson and Merryweather) who also worked Old Brandley, Barrow, Stoneycroft, Thornthwaite and the ill-fated Cobalt Mine. The company took the Tebay shaft to 30 fathoms, but because the water-wheel was no longer able to cope with the deluge of water had it replaced by a 30 hp steam engine driving 9 in force pumps. The water-wheel was thereafter used to drive a saw mill and some crushing equipment.

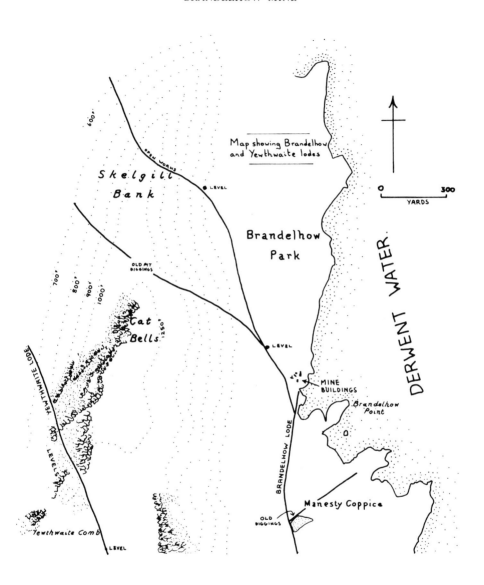

Map showing Brandelhow and Yewthwaite lodes

Skelgill Bank

Brandelhow Park

DERWENT WATER

Cat Bells

Yewthwaite Comb

Manesty Coppice

Mine Buildings

Brandelhow Point

    In the early 1850s the 20 fathom level N hit a rich deposit of ore and here, it was decided, the future of the mine lay. Accordingly the New Engine Shaft was sunk and by 1853 was down 30 fathoms. At this point the engine was transferred to the new shaft and sinking continued. By 1855 this was down

40 fathoms but the company found the work costly, for not only was the ground particularly hard, but additionally large quantities of salt-water were pouring from the 30 and 40 fathom levels simultaneously being driven forward. Fortunately perseverance was rewarded for access was gained to some good deposits and for the next few years the mine yielded approximately 250 tons of ore per annum.

By 1860 the Keswick Mining Company had withdrawn from all its other mining ventures and was now in the hands of a new set of partners (Charles Dear and associates), but the Brandlehow mine continued to be worked for another three years, producing 290 tons per annum. The year 1863 saw operations suspended as a result of a row between directors and shareholders: it would appear that a new engine was required and, to the shareholders who had already lost money in the company's other ventures, this new call for capital was asking too much. By 1864 the mine had filled with water, and in 1865 was abandoned.

In 1870 Messrs H. K. Spark and B. Plummer, two gentlemen with interests in many of the Derwent mines, took a lease on Brandlehow, but in this as in all their other mining ventures were remarkably unsuccessful.

In 1883 the mine was acquired by the Brandley Mining Company, an organisation run by Henry Burrow Vercoe, a mining engineer from Portinscale (see also Yewthwaite and Barrow). Operations got off to a flying start and by 1885 some 265 tons of ore had been raised from the 40, 50, and 60 fathom levels. In 1886, 113 tons of ore was raised, but before the year's end all work ceased and the mine was allowed to flood.

Vercoe transferred his lease to a new set of partners (Messrs Jennings, White and Miller) and the year of 1887 was spent in pumping out water and putting the workings back in order. A 350 hp engine was erected in 1888 to cope with the increasing quantity of water for by now the mine was 70 fathoms down. Over the next three years a total of 250 tons of ore was raised but this was a poor amount which could hardly have covered the cost of the engine and its heavy fuel consumption. Early in 1891 the mine was abandoned.

Old Brandley Mine

A small lead mine with most of its workings on the E flank of Skelgill Bank (NY 247204). The oldest part is on the top of the hill where some openworks and an open shaft can be seen. Below this are four levels, the one of most recent date being the lowest at 600 ft A.O.D. The mine was worked, rather infrequently, by the lessees of Brandlehow Mine.

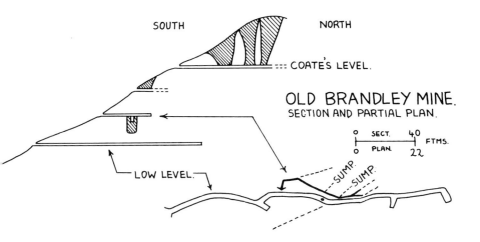

OLD BRANDLEY MINE.
SECTION AND PARTIAL PLAN.

Mining Details

The mine is on the Brandlehow Lode which is either divided or has a small off-shoot at this point. Some of the workings may be on one branch, some on the other, but no records have survived to clarify matters. From the plans it would appear that a reasonable quantity of ore was found at the top of the hill, the yield decreasing with depth. The ore contained 7 ozs of silver per ton of lead metal. Fluorite was found in abundance in the upper levels, a very rare gangue mineral in the Lake District.

History

The openworks belong to pre-gunpowder days and nothing is known about them (see, however, Minersputt). There is good reason to believe that the Coate's Level and the two below it were driven by John Tebay; if so, this would place the work between the years 1819 and 1835. The Low or New Level was driven by the Keswick Mining Company in about 1850 but soon given up for want of success. In 1873 Messrs H. K. Spark and B. Plummer re-opened the bottom two levels and did a little prospecting work. Nothing has been done since.

Barrow Mine

An extensive and very old lead mine with workings on both sides of the Braithwaite to Buttermere road. Most of the early workings are situated on the W side of the road (NY 232222), these being responsible for the huge

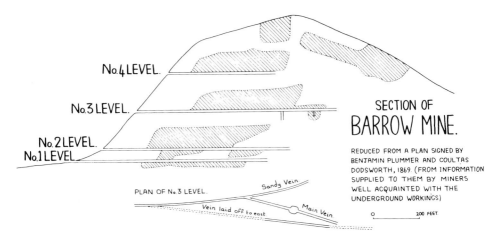

SECTION OF
BARROW MINE.

REDUCED FROM A PLAN SIGNED BY
BENJAMIN PLUMMER AND COULTAS
DODSWORTH, 1869. (FROM INFORMATION
SUPPLIED TO THEM BY MINERS
WELL ACQUAINTED WITH THE
UNDERGROUND WORKINGS)

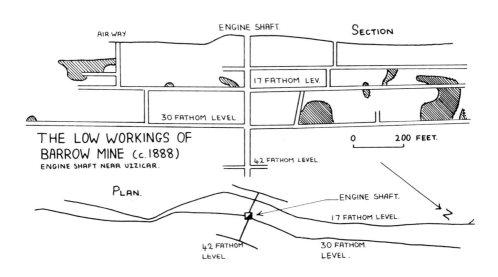

fan of spoil sweeping down the hill side. The later workings are in the neighbourhood of Uzzicar on the E side of the road (NY 234217). Mining ceased in 1889.

Mining Details

The Barrow Lode courses approximately 20° W of N and is believed to be part of one large vein, the Yewthwaite and Thornthwaite Lodes being others. At the mine the vein is divided into two parallel branches roughly 17 fathoms apart. The W branch, or Sand Vein, is almost perpendicular, whereas the E, or main branch, hades slightly to the E. The Sand Vein contained a great quantity of friable quartz and was most dangerous to work since, if great care was not taken, the quartz would indeed flow like sand, filling up the workings within a few minutes. The main vein was much more solid. The predominant ore was argentiferous galena with subsidiary amounts of blende, cerussite, pyromorphite and iron pyrite. The mine was a wet one, presumably as a result of the particularly permeable nature of the vein-stuff.

History

The earliest document relating to this mine is a letter from mining engineer David Davies to Prince Charles, Duke of Somerset. Davies was involved in mining activities throughout the Derwent Fells (1680s) and took a particular interest in Goldscope and Barrow. The letter is informative and worth displaying in its entirety:-

At a hill called Barrow we first got ore, after the lease was taken, where ye old man had wrought before, but he was outed by too much water and too little air. When we got in we gave it air and pumped out ye water and when we came to ye old mans work we found no ore. Then we sank 10 fathoms deeper and found none. Then we drove north and south upon a level 20 fathoms each way, but none or very little ore was found. Then we did drive into ye east side and found good quality ore lying safe in sand which sunk down into ye hill from which we pumped water 40 fathoms to ye day, and brought down the air in wooden pipes 40 fathoms, but last season came on at Michaelmas that the water was too strong for us. We conclude to bring up a level to clear ye water. We set upon a level 28 fathoms deeper in ye hill than the sole of ye work, and on a perpendicular from ye top of ye hill 70 fathoms and we had to drive before we came under the sole of ye work 300 fathoms and we wrought this level night and day for seven years. It cost upwards of £900 and when we came to clear ye work of ye water ye ore did not continue 2 fathoms deeper, but we found ore on our way which did help us on.

In this level as we went we found ore in our sole, but we could not work it for water. Then we got on another level 26 fathoms beneath that and have driven that for 140 fathoms where our main work is now, in which we found ore in diverse places betwixt us and the first level which is all the ore of any consequence we get at present.

We find ore in the bottom of this present work which we call ye middle drift and have set on another drift 6 fathoms deeper than that and have driven for 50 fathoms and had ore for 20 fathoms, and ore is sunk down deeper than our level but watered. We tried to clear it with pumps but the water was too strong for us so we left that off and set off on another level as low as we could get which is 12 fathoms deeper than any of ye former. This level is out of ye vein and we have driven it 70 fathoms and have sunk two shafts upon it and are sinking ye third. We have been working it for 2 years and hope to get into ye vein in less than a year. This hath cost me already £350 and when this is up, ye whole hill will be cleared of water and may be passed from one drift to another, so that if ye ore prove good it may last a good work for 40 years without the charge of any other levels and may be constantly aired at easy charge from the drift above.

To what extent the hopes of Davies were realised is not known.

Various people held and worked the mine during the 18th century but no really informative details are available.

During the 1830s Barrow was leased by John Tebay who had an interest in most of the Derwent mines but the delapidated state in which it was found seems to have discouraged him from doing anything with it.

In 1847 it was acquired by the Keswick Mining Company which worked most of the mines in the area. Levels 2 and 4 were re-opened and by 1854 these were fully cleared and timbered. From 1854 to 1857 a total of 300 tons of ore was extracted which in turn yielded 1,700 ozs of silver, but this was from old ground left by the ancients. By 1858 all easily accessible ore had been removed and the decision had to be taken whether to abandon the mine or sink capital into exploration. The company, which in any case had financial problems, opted for the former and the mine was closed.

The mine was taken in 1870 by Messrs H. K. Spark and B. Plummer, who over the next three years did some prospecting and extended the number 3 level. Nothing, as always, came of their efforts and the miners were transferred to Yewthwaite, another of their mines.

In 1883, Henry Vercoe (see also Brandlehow and Yewthwaite) formed the Barrow Mining Company and sank a shaft at the base of the mountain. By 1886 the workings were 30 fathoms down and a 60 ft, 75 hp water-wheel had been erected for dressing and pumping. This wheel must have been quite something to see. In 1887 the company was in liquidation and the lease assigned to a newly-formed partnership called the Braithwaite Mining Company. The new company took the shaft to 42 fathoms, but in 1889 it too was in liquidation. During the period 1886 to 1888 only 210 tons of lead ore and 21 tons of blende were raised. On the 2nd January 1896 all the plant and machinery was sold.

Stoneycroft Mine

A small and infrequently-worked lead mine a few yards to the W of the bridge over Stoneycroft Gill on the Braithwaite to Buttermere road (NY 231212). The early workings were open cuts in the bed of the gill from which the water was diverted by a dam and watercourse cut out of the solid rock. This watercourse is still visible and rejoins the stream a few feet from the western side of Stoneycroft Bridge. The later workings were reached by a shaft. No work has been done since 1854.

Mining Details

At the mine, the Stoneycroft Lode courses 75° W of N, hades to the N at about 1 fathom in 6 and is believed to be a continuation of the southern off-shoot of the Brandlehow Lode. The ore was argentiferous galena (22 ozs silver per ton of lead metal) in a matrix of friable quartz and smashed rock. The width of the vein varied between 1 ft and 4 ft.

The shaft was sunk where the lode crosses the stream and a few hundred yards to the W of this point, but not on the Stoneycroft Lode, is a level on the S bank (NY 230211). The level has collapsed 10 ft in from the entrance and therefore its full length is unknown. A level may also be seen by the side of the watercourse; this one is only a few feet long. About ¾ of a mile to the NW of Stoneycroft, at the head of Barrow Gill, are some ancient workings which may be on a continuation of the Stoneycroft Lode, but no information relating to these has been found.

History

The earliest record of what may very well be Stoneycroft Mine is a letter from David Davies to Prince Charles, Duke of Somerset. Davies worked a number of the Derwent mines in the 1680s to 1690s. The letter reads:-

> At Mine Gill we wrought 10 fathoms into ye hill where we found ore a foot thick, but went not far endwise into ye hill, but sunk right down which we followed 7 fathoms deeper, then ye brook came in* and left ore going down still, but the water was too strong for our pumps, so we left it off about 7 years since having got a good quantity of ore there.

In 1847 the mine was leased by the Keswick Mining Company (Messrs Langton, Richardson and Merryweather) which, like its predecessors, di-verted the stream and took the shaft to 20 fathoms below surface. A pre-existing 10 fathom level off the shaft was extended another 15 to 20 fathoms S, but as little ore was found new levels were driven at the 15 and 20 fathom horizons. In these the ore content was also poor. The water was removed by means of a 22 ft water-wheel driving 6 in pumps, and the ore lifted by manual labour (though later a horse whim was used for this purpose). There were dressing floors but no crushing plant.

In 1853 the company started to sink the shaft another 6 fathoms to expose some ore that had been seen in the sole of the 20 fathom level, but in 1854 all work stopped as a result of mounting financial losses. In the six year period a total of 6 tons of ore was raised.

* In Postlethwaite's *Mines and Mining in the English Lake District*, a story is told of a dam-burst which flooded the shaft and buried the miners under sand and mud. Mr Wildridge of Workington who has done so much research on the very early history of these mines tells the author that Davies' letter is the only original reference he has found to a flood, so unless somebody discovers otherwise a date of *c.* 1690 is claimed for the event.

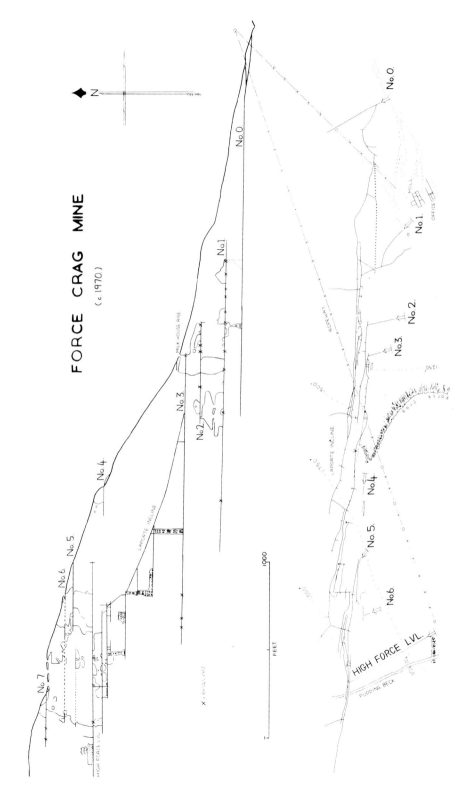

FORCE CRAG MINE

(c 1970.)

Force Crag Mine

A lead, zinc and baryte mine situated at the head of the Coledale Valley about 2½ miles SW of Braithwaite. External examination shows two apparently distinct areas of activity; the High Force Workings (NY 193214) and the Low Force Workings (NY 200216), but internally these are connected by a substantial tunnel, the Laporte Incline. Though both workings are on the same vein the composition of the veinstuff at each site is quite different; the upper part was worked for baryte, the lower mainly for zinc. The mine is one of the few in the Lake District to have been worked with reasonable regularity throughout this century. The present occupant is New Coledale Mining Ltd.

Mining Details

The Force Crag Vein courses E-W, has a hade of about 1 fathom in 3 to the N and is believed to run from the head of Coledale to Lanthwaite Green near Crummock Water. The low workings, levels 0, 1, 2 and 3, yielded baryte, blende and galena (35 ozs silver per ton of lead metal) in the ratio of approximately 30:10:1, whilst the upper ones yielded mainly baryte with subsidiary amounts of psilomelane. The early workings were largely confined to level 3 and below, as baryte did not become saleable until the late 1860s. As demand for baryte grew, however, the high workings were progressively opened out. For a long time, the movement of baryte from the high workings to the head of the valley road was a source of much difficulty and inconvenience, but in 1940 an aerial ropeway was constructed. This in turn was replaced in 1950 by a costly but much more permanent internal incline.

A particular problem in the early days of the mine was the separation of intermingled blende and baryte. These two minerals have very similar densities which rendered the old-fashioned method of gravity separation almost totally ineffective. The problem was solved in 1914 with the erection of a flotation plant by which time a considerable amount of blende had ended up on the spoil heaps.

History

The existence of an ore analysis report dated 1578 shows that the ancients were certainly aware of a silver-lead vein at Coledale Head, but to what degree they exploited it is not known.

John Tebay, the holder of many of the Derwent mines, also held this one, the only information available being that in 1839 he sub-let to a Messrs Airey and Cowper.

On 21st June 1848 a lease was granted to Messrs Cowper, Walton and Dowthwaite (see Threlkeld Mine and High Brow Sulphur Mine). At this time levels 2 and 3 were already in existence and all worthwhile ore above them had been extracted by earlier occupants. Accordingly the company commenced the driving of a new low adit, No. 1, to exploit the deposits which were seen going below No. 2. By 1855 the level was 300 yards long, and in 1863 had reached 580 yards. Unfortunately this long and costly drive yielded only 350 tons of ore so in 1863 or soon after the mine was abandoned.

In 1867 the mine was taken by Messrs Hall and Straughton who were interested solely in baryte. In 1869 they were working levels 1 and 5 and demand for the product was brisk. A by-product of the work in No. 1 was a small amount of lead-bearing material, which was – there being no dressing plant – simply thrown onto the dumps. The baryte from the high levels was swept by water down long wooden chutes fastened to the face of Force Crag and in 1873 a tramway to run from the mine to Braithwaite was constructed to facilitate the second part of the journey.

By 1874 levels 6 and 7 had been opened out and further extensive deposits of baryte found. In 1879 the demand for the mineral fell and little work was done thereafter. In 1885 a little maintenance work was being done, but in 1886 the mine was abandoned completely.

The company, which later operated under the name of Force Crag Mining Company (1876-1879) and subsequently the Force Crag Lead and Barytes Company (1880), raised a total of 4,500 tons of baryte.

In 1906 Messrs Joseph Lobb and Thomas Dennison (Cumberland Mines Ltd) worked levels 1, 2 and 3, but as there was no income to be made from lead, zinc became the primary concern. Unfortunately their gravity dressing plant was incapable of processing blende contaminated with baryte so much of the ore ended up on the dumps, and in 1909 the company went into liquidation.

The next occupant, in 1912, was the Coledale Syndicate which spent a considerable amount of money in re-opening levels 1 and 2 and on the installation, in 1914, of an Elmore flotation plant. For the first time it became possible to separate blende and baryte, but in 1915 the company exhausted its capital and the mine was closed.

Braithwaite Mines Ltd commenced in 1916 to work blende from 1 and 2 levels, but the disastrous post-war drop in the price of zinc, which caused the closing of Thornthwaite Mine, also forced this company out of business and the mine closed in 1923. Braithwaite Mines Ltd had started the No. 0 level but had not reached the vein by the time of closure.

In 1930 the Derwent Fells Mineral Company drove the new High Force Level exposing a massive deposit of baryte, but this was not exploited until Tampimex Oil Products Ltd took the mine in 1939. The latter built the aerial ropeway and raised a total of 35,000 tons of baryte. By 1947 they had sunk 80 ft below the High Force Level but the severe winter of that year caused the workings to flood and all the pumping machinery was lost.

The mine was next taken by Laporte Chemicals who drove an internal incline to connect the No. 3 level with the workings below the High Force Level. Shortly afterwards, however, a drop in the price of baryte caused the mine to close.

In 1960 the new occupants, McKechnie Brothers, extended the No. 3 level hoping to find a downward continuation of the baryte in the higher workings, but it turned out that the deposit had deteriorated with depth. Their last trial was to drive the High Force Level forward and in so doing discovered a new deposit of baryte. In 1966 they withdrew from mining.

In 1967, as a result of favourable reports by the mining engineer, W. T. Shaw, Force Crag Mines Ltd of Toronto was formed. The company was primarily interested in lead and zinc and accordingly commenced exploratory work in the lower levels in order to evaluate reserves. These efforts were fairly short-lived and it was not until January 1977 that work was restarted by Force Crag Mines (U.K.) Ltd, a subsidiary of New Force Crag Mines Ltd, a reconstruction of the Toronto company. A major feature of this work was the sinking of a 30 metre shaft from the sole of 0 level, carried out under the auspices of R. I. Gunn.

The aim of the company was to identify an ore body of at least 100,000 tons containing 10% lead and zinc, which if found would have justified the installation of a new dressing plant, the old plant at that time being in a derelict state. However, the prevailing low prices of lead and zinc never justified the injection of capital required to render the mine productive, and sometime in 1977 all work was stopped.

In 1978 an attempt to work the mine was made by R. I. Gunn, a former employee of Force Crag Mines (U.K.) Ltd. Gunn was aware, because of his previous experience, that large scale working was simply not viable, but felt that small scale operation stood a good chance of success. He formed a company, Braithwaite Mining Ltd, and commenced a determined programme of exploration. The mill was completely refurbished and an inclined shaft cut between No. 1 and No. 2 levels. The company was on the threshold of going into production when, in 1982, financial problems intervened and all work stopped. On 1st July 1982 all plant and equipment was auctioned.

In May 1984 the mine was taken by New Coledale Mining Ltd (Messrs P. Blezard, M. Sutcliffe and L. Greenbank). Initial efforts were directed into the refurbishment of buildings and the making ready of Nos. 0 and 1 levels. It is the intention of the company to mine blende from No. 1 stope in No. 1 level and baryte from No. 0 level.

Cobalt Mine

To this mine goes the dubious distinction of having been the worst mining investment in the whole of the district. It is situated in rough steep ground a little to the NE of Scar Crag (NY 206207)

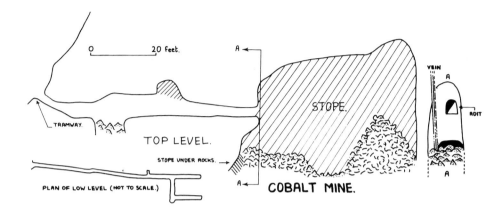

It lies on a N-S vein and, although the vein-stuff presents visible signs of cobalt mineralisation, analysis shows there to be very little indeed. The vein does, however, contain a good deal of arsenic. There are supposed to be four levels, but only three are known to the author.

The mine was opened *c.* 1848 by the Keswick Mining Company which constructed a road from Stoneycroft and erected a very expensive dressing plant – all before the mine had been opened up. How long the mine worked is not known but the total output is supposed to have been only a few ounces of the pure mineral.

Early this century Thornthwaite Mines showed an interest in re-opening it for prospecting, but this was never done.

Embleton Mine

A small lead mine situated about 250 yards NE of the Blue Bell Inn in the village of Embleton (NY 169306). It was abandoned in 1856. The vein courses N-S and though highly mineralised contained little lead.

The only record of mining prior to 1853 is a lease granted to a Peter How and others enabling them to mine in Embleton and Setmurthy. Whether or not the mine existed prior to this date (1749) is not known. In 1853 persons unknown leased the mine, cleared it out and drove the middle level, raising, in 1855, $10\frac{1}{2}$ tons of ore. This sold for £126, a yield insufficient to make the mine pay: accordingly it was closed.

About $1\frac{1}{2}$ miles to the E of Embleton Mine there is a run-in level behind Close House (NY 182309). This trial, for which no information is available, was almost certainly made by one of the lessees of Embleton Mine.

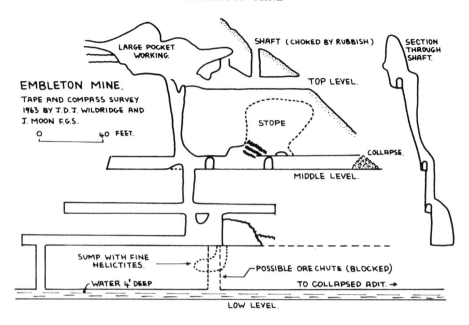

EMBLETON MINE.
TAPE AND COMPASS SURVEY
1963 BY J.D.J. WILDRIDGE AND
J. MOON F.G.S.

Thornthwaite Mines

(Ladstock Mine, Rachel Wood Mine, Thornthwaite Mine, Beckstones Mine)

The Thornthwaite sett lies between Braithwaite and the S bank of Beckstones Gill. Within it are four distinct mines, Ladstock (NY 220251), Rachel Wood (NY 223256), Thornthwaite (NY 223258) and Beckstones (NY 219263). Ladstock, Beckstones and the outcrop workings of Rachel Wood are very old and were abandoned some time in the 1870s. Thornthwaite and the deep workings of Rachel Wood are more recent and were abandoned in December 1920. The mine yielded the ores of lead and zinc.

Mining Details

A number of veins traverse the property but only four are of importance: the Ladstock East Lode, Ladstock West Lode, Rachel Wood Lode and Thornthwaite Lode.

The two Ladstock lodes were wrought at the Ladstock Mine by shafts,

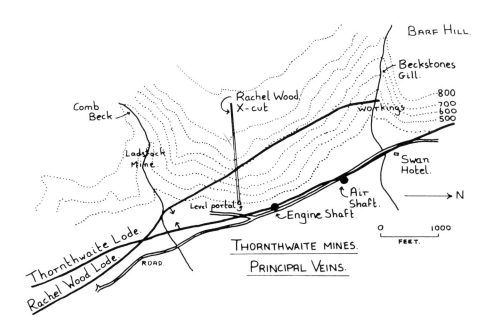

THORNTHWAITE MINES.
PRINCIPAL VEINS.

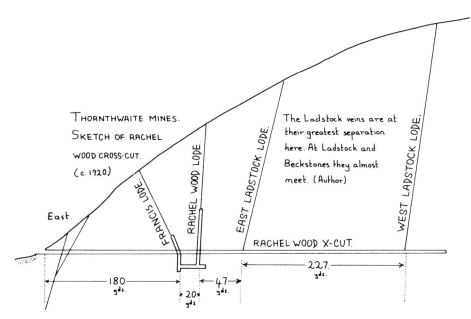

THORNTHWAITE MINES.
SKETCH OF RACHEL
WOOD CROSS-CUT.
(c. 1920.)

The Ladstock veins are at their greatest separation here. At Ladstock and Beckstones they almost meet. (Author)

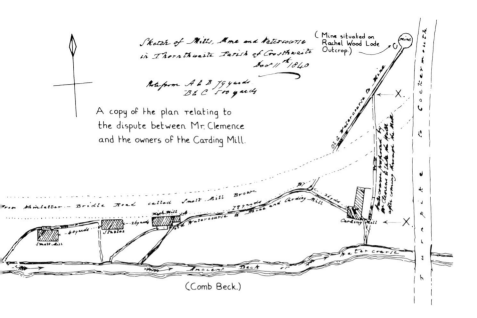

Sketch of Mills, Mine and Watercourse
in Thornthwaite Parish of Crosthwaite
Dec 11th 1840

Distance from A to B 79 yards
B to C 500 yards

(Mine situated on
Rachel Wood Lode
Outcrop.)

A copy of the plan relating to
the dispute between Mr. Clemence
and the owners of the Carding Mill.

(Comb Beck.)

openworks and levels near the banks of Comb Beck. At the mine the lodes
are parallel, course 10° W of N and hade to the E at 1 fathom in 3. The
widths are about 3 ft and the ore was galena in a matrix of smashed rock
with a little quartz. The length of their northern continuation is not known
with certainty, but an old map shows them crossing Beckstones Gill near to
the point at which the Rachel Wood Lode crosses.

The Rachel Wood Lode courses 30° W of N, hades to the W at about 1
fathom in 2, yielded blende and galena, and runs the whole length of the
sett. It was originally worked at outcrop by pits and shallow levels, all of
which are pre-1870 and some very ancient indeed. Later, in 1875, a cross-
cut level (the Rachel Wood Cross-Cut) was driven to explore the vein in
depth and follows a straight line directed 5° S of W. The level portal is at
the grid reference already quoted, just below the forest track called Seldom
Seen Road on the Thornthwaite Forest visitors' map. At 180 yards in the
cross-cut strikes a relatively minor vein called the Francis Lode, and a few
yards further on intersects the Rachel Wood Lode. From the section it will
be seen that a considerable area of ground has been stoped from the latter.
The cross-cut was continued for another 370 yards in the hope of intersecting
further veins, but nothing of value was found.

The Beckstones Mine was nothing more than a small group of shallow
pits exploiting the Rachel Wood and possibly Ladstock lodes.

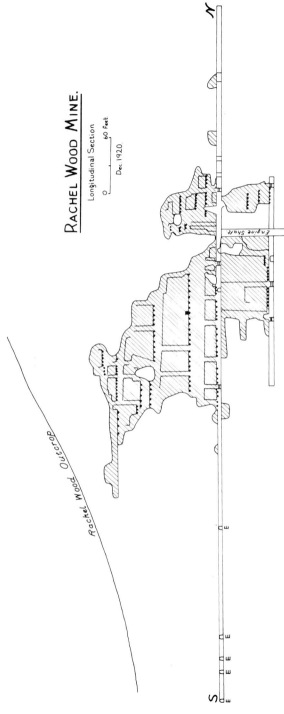

RACHEL WOOD MINE.

Longitudinal Section

Dec. 1920.

0   60 Feet

Rachel Wood Outcrop

Engine Shaft

N

S

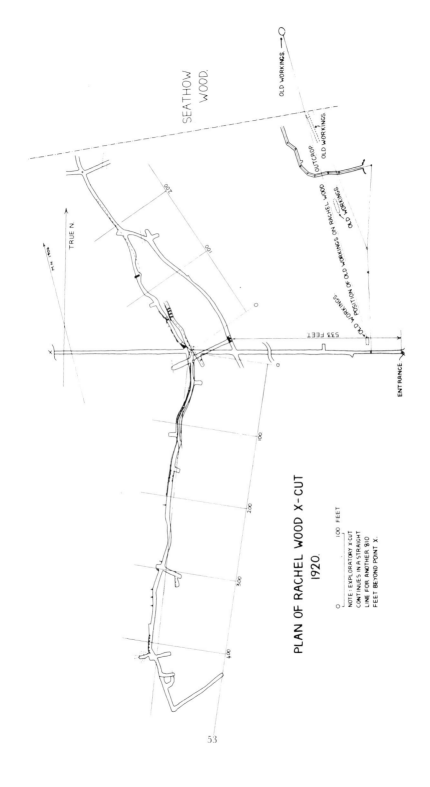

PLAN OF RACHEL WOOD X-CUT
1920.

SEATHOW WOOD.

TRUE N.

M.N. 1906

OLD WORKINGS.

OUTCROP

OLD WORKINGS

OLD WORKINGS

POSITION OF OLD WORKINGS ON RACHEL WOOD

OLD WORKINGS

OLD WORKINGS

533 FEET

ENTRANCE

0   100 FEET

NOTE:-EXPLORATORY X CUT
CONTINUES IN A STRAIGHT
LINE FOR ANOTHER 810
FEET BEYOND POINT X.

53

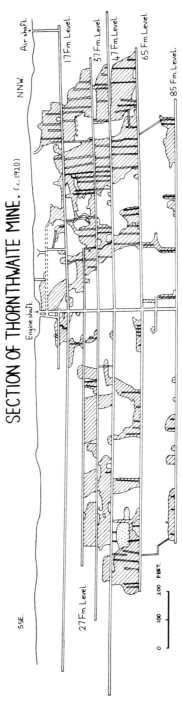

SECTION OF THORNTHWAITE MINE. (c. 1920)

NNW. Air shaft.

17 Fm. Level.

37 Fm. Level.

47 Fm. Level.

65 Fm. Level.

85 Fm. Level.

Engine shaft.

SSE.

27 Fm. Level.

0   100   200 FEET.

54

The Thornthwaite Lode is believed to be the northern continuation of the Yewthwaite and Barrow lodes. It hades 1 fathom in 3 to the E and courses approximately 20° W of N. The upper part contained a large amount of cerussite and dark brown gossan – deeper down galena and blende were the dominant ores (silver yield 10 ozs per ton of lead metal). The vein was very ill-defined in that it was hard to say where vein ended and country-rock began. The gangue was smashed rock and rock decomposition products with a small amount of quartz. The mine was worked from the engine shaft which is now situated directly under Thornthwaite Garage; in fact part of that establishment is composed of the lower part of the pit head structure.

History

The origins of the mine are obscure and not that much is known about its later history. It was certainly worked in the 18th century but the first interesting details come from some old documents relating to a legal action. Evidently the mines on the Rachel Wood outcrop were worked by persons unknown up to 1826, and power for the workings came from a wheel which took water from a watercourse (B.C. on the plan). Now when the mine was abandoned the owners of the Carding Mill, who hitherto had taken some of the water for their wheel, diverted all of it to their works which was fine until a Mr Clemence leased the old mine in 1840. The question arose as to whether or not the new lessee had a right to redirect water for his use. The court ruled in Clemence's favour, but for the mutual convenience of both parties it was probable that the compromise solution (XX on the plan) was adopted. It is also known that Clemence was working Thornthwaite Lode and that by 1844 he had sunk 17 fathoms below surface. At this time there was a 22 ft water-wheel above the engine shaft and the water from this wheel fed a smaller one. It is not certain for how long Clemence occupied the sett but it is known that he was hampered by a lack of capital.

In 1848 the Keswick Mining Company took over (see also Brandlehow, Old Brandley, Barrow, Stoneycroft and Cobalt Mines), erecting a 40 ft water-wheel over the Thornthwaite shaft. This company also re-washed the dumps of Beckstones, but operations could not have lasted for more than twelve years for by 1860 Brandlehow was the only mine it worked.

In 1869 the lease was taken by one William Francis and in 1872 a company called 'The Keswick United Silver-Lead Mines Company' was formed with Francis as manager. The Rachel Wood Cross-Cut was started in 1875 but work ceased before the lode was reached. Some work was also done at Ladstock and Beckstones but by the mid-'70s all efforts were confined to the Thornthwaite Mine. From January 1872 to December 1878 the company sold only 164 tons of blende and a much smaller quantity of lead ore giving a total income of £650. This hardly covered office expenses never mind anything else and in 1879 the shareholders were unwilling to support the venture any longer. The mine, which was now 27 fathoms down, closed.

The lease was transferred to Messrs Francis M. Robertson and Thomas J. Clements, but in December 1882 was re-assigned to Messrs Henry Lobb and Michael Reed who formed Cumberland Lead Mines Ltd. For a long time this company seems to have done very little but in 1890, and for the next four years of its existence, a yearly average of about 700 tons of blende and 400 tons of lead ore was produced.

In 1894 the mine was taken by F. W. Crewdson and Anthony Wilson who in 1900 formed a company called Thornthwaite Mines Ltd. Under their leadership and using the best technology of the day, the mine flourished, maintaining a yearly output similar to that of the previous company. The Thornthwaite mine was sunk to 85 fathoms and the Rachel Wood Cross-Cut driven forward to the main lode and beyond. After the first World War there was a severe fall in the price of lead and zinc and in 1920 all mining stopped.

Anthony Wilson (b. 1871-d. 1953) was also involved with the Threlkeld and Carrock Fell Mine and acted as consultant to many other mines in the N of England. After Thornthwaite closed he used its water power to generate electricity for his own house, Thornthwaite Grange, and several other houses in Braithwaite and Thornthwaite. A commemorative plaque to Wilson and his wife can be seen in the bus shelter at Thornthwaite.

Barf Mines
(Beckstones Level, Windyhill Mine, Woodend Mine)

The sett is a large one, extending from the N bank of Beckstones Gill to the S bank of Beck Wythop. Within the sett lie three very small lead and zinc mines, the Beckstones Level (NY 218263), Windyhill Mine (NY 219267) and Woodend Mine (NY 219271). Between these are various small trials and level grassy patches which may have been the sites of old mine buildings. Nothing has been done since 1891.

Mining Details

These mines exploited the northern continuation of the Thornthwaite Lode yielding blende, cerussite and small amounts of galena. The vein was tapped by shallow levels, pits and trenches on its back. An analysis of the lead ore showed a silver content of 8 ozs per ton of lead metal.

History

The first known records of this sett, Michaelmas 1532, show it to have been worked by three Derbyshire miners. No further records appear to exist prior to 1754 in which year it was leased by one Anthony Tissington who worked the sett for about ten years and raised 31 tons of ore. In 1770 the lease was taken by a Mrs Piels who appears to have worked the mines until 1783. The amount of ore raised is not known as the lady also leased Barrow Mine and the ore from both locations was combined into a single figure.

Between 1812 and 1857 the mines were probably leased in conjunction with Barrow and Brandlehow and, although a little work is known to have been done, the annual output probably never exceeded ten tons. In 1858 Messrs Fuller and Company did a little prospecting work but nothing ever came of it. Within the period from 1888 to 1892, William Francis (ex-manager of Thornthwaite) attempted to open out the mines and the Barf and Woodend Silver, Lead and Blende Company was formed, but other than a little tidying up nothing more was done, mainly through lack of capital.

Borrowdale Graphite Mine

A very famous mine with a long, complicated and colourful history. It is situated on the hillside a little to the NW of Seathwaite (NY 232125). A great deal has been written about this mine, much of it vague, and seemingly no-one has yet succeeded in putting together a really comprehensive account of its history. Equally ill-furnished, the author merely offers some of the less speculative features of its past.

Even the date of last working is not certain, for although official statistics show that a ton of graphite was removed in 1876 and none thereafter, the mine was nevertheless in the hands of a private company right up to 1891, therefore it seems likely that some work was done after 1876.

Mining Details

The graphite is associated with a dyke of highly altered diorite (300 fathoms long in a NNW/SSE direction) bounded by two masses of compact blue diabase. There are numerous quartz veins and strings traversing this formation and, although these are often discoloured with graphite, the big deposits, in the form of pipes, occur some distance away from the veins. The pipes are randomly distributed throughout the diabase and to a lesser extent the diorite; this made the mining a difficult and haphazard affair.

The only effective way to locate pipes was by driving long and tortuous exploratory tunnels. Thus the output of the mine tended to be sporadic, prolonged periods of no output whatsoever being quite common. Not surprisingly, therefore, this mine is a maze and the illustrated section of it appearing in several books (and reproduced here) presents a gross over-simplification of its true interior.

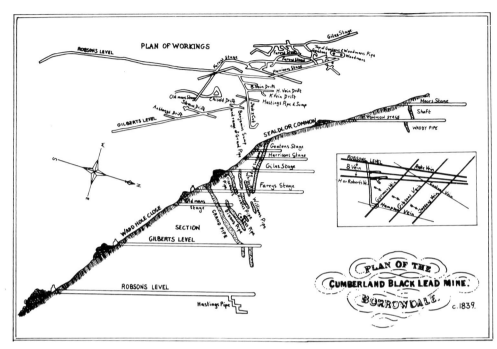

A recent explanation of the origin of the deposits is that the graphite, an allotrope of carbon, orginated from carbon monoxide gas $2CO \rightleftharpoons CO_2 + C$, the reaction being catalysed by iron oxides, pyrite, iron silicates and quartz (Strens, 1965). The source of all this carbon monoxide, however, is not clear.

The graphite from this mine has been variously named Black Cawke, Wad, Black Lead and Plumbago and found a number of applications. In the early days it was used for marking sheep and rust-proofing stoves. Taken in conjunction with ale or wine it was a panacea for an absurdly wide variety of ills, though its poisonous metallic compounds content probably made the patient feel a good deal worse! The prime uses, however, seem to have been in crucible and refractory mould construction, as a separating agent in metal casting and, of course, pencil making. The Borrowdale Mine is well-known for being responsible for the birth of the Keswick pencil industry in about 1790, an event which rather curiously came quite late in the mine's history.

Two of the graphite pipes outcrop and these were where mining first took place. The higher outcrop is on Gorton's (or Goaton's) Pipe and it would seem that the very earliest work was done here. This working – a pit – was known as Upper Wadhole and by 1555 was already very deep. The lower is on the Grand Pipe and is said to have been discovered sometime in Elizabeth I's reign when a storm-uprooted ash tree exposed the graphite below. This location was known as the lower Wadhole.

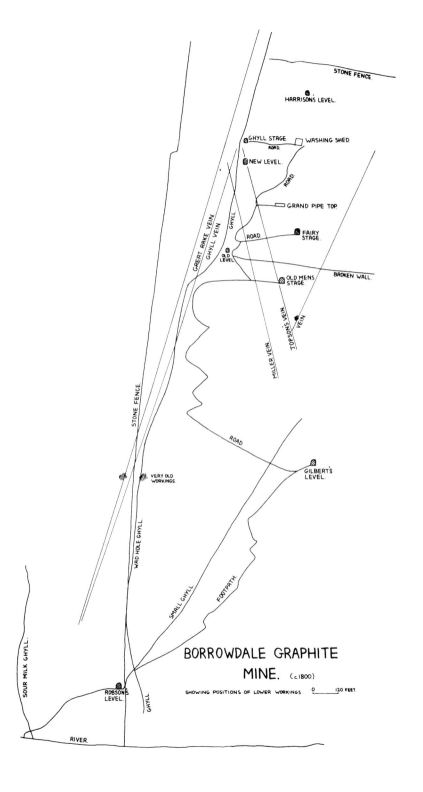

STONE FENCE.

HARRISONS LEVEL.

GHYLL STAGE   WASHING SHED.
ROAD.
NEW LEVEL.

ROAD.

GRAND PIPE TOP

ROAD.   FAIRY
             STAGE.

OLD
LEVEL.

OLD MENS
STAGE.   BROKEN WALL.

VEIN.

GREAT RAKE VEIN.
GHYLL VEIN.
GHYLL.

MILLER VEIN.
TOPSON'S VEIN.

STONE FENCE.

ROAD.

VERY OLD.
WORKINGS.   GILBERT'S
                               LEVEL.

WAD HOLE GHYLL.

SMALL GHYLL.
FOOTPATH.

SOUR MILK GHYLL.

BORROWDALE GRAPHITE
MINE. (c.1800)

ROBSON'S
LEVEL.

GHYLL.

SHOWING POSITIONS OF LOWER WORKINGS.   0   120 FEET.

RIVER.

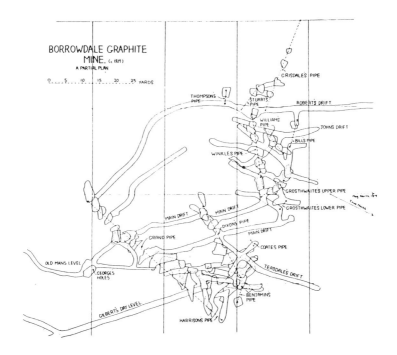

Gilbert's Stage or Level, which drains the main body of the mine, was driven between the years 1798 and 1800. Robson's Level was the last major work (c. 1820).

History

On 26 August 1555, two Royal commissioners, Thomas Legh and Nicholas Bardsey, were instructed to visit Borrowdale and report on, among other things, any wad hole 'for the colouring or uring of sheep'. Their subsequent report tells of a wad hole on Seatoller Common (Upper Wadhole) indicating it to have reached such a depth that flooding made the removal of graphite a rather hazardous business. In December 1555 as a result of this report the Crown granted a 21 year lease to Ambrose Dormer, son of Sir Michael Dormer, Lord Mayor of London 1541-2. Dormer died eleven years later and nothing is known of his activities or the subsequent fate of the lease.

In 1578 a new lease to the wad holes and some other properties was taken by a Roger Robinson. In 1594 this passed into the hands of a Mathew Buck, thence to be acquired in 1607 by Messrs Edward Boraston and Thomas Fanshaw. These two gentlemen subsequently sub-let to Daniel and Emanuel Hechstetter of Mines Royal, but unfortunately nothing is known about the work done by any of these people. The Hechstetters held the lease until 1625 (note that as the Mines Royal charter did not include reference to graphite the Hechstetters had no automatic right to the mine).

Around 1613-14, James I sold considerable areas of land in Lincolnshire and the Furness Abbey Manor of Borrowdale to Messrs William Whitmore and Jonas Verdon who in turn sold the land to existing tenants. The Borrowdale sale in 1614 included the wad holes subsequently to be sold to Messrs William Lamplugh and Charles Hudson. It should of course be remembered that at all times the mining rights were held by the Hechstetters, such rights being unaffected by change of ownership. In due course the mining property descended in two moieties. One was purchased on the 9th March 1622 by London lawyer, Sir John Bankes, the other remaining in the Hudson family until acquired in two parts, in 1697 and 1706 respectively, by one John Shepheard. In 1625 Bankes purchased the Hechstetter lease, which still had eleven years to run, and started mining for himself.

The Shepheard and Bankes families ran the mine as joint proprietors until the 28th February 1758 when John Shepheard's son let his moiety on a 99 year lease to a group of London gentlemen. The Bankes moiety stayed within that family until very recently.

It is known that as early as the 16th century there existed a good market for graphite, the prices quoted in a lawsuit of 1597 being £13 6s. 8d. and £5 6s. 8d. per ton for superior and inferior quality respectively. During the 17th century and later the graphite was sold at irregular intervals in transactions – called bargains – between the proprietors and certain approved merchants. One reason for this irregularity was the unpredictable nature of the mine itself, but another was to keep the selling price high by means of an artificially-induced rarity. The markedly various charges for the graphite are astonishing, and the following are some examples taken from records of sales all of which refer to the price per ton for superior quality: 1646, £18; 1671, £100; 1761, £1,344; 1804, £3,920. Not surprisingly these high prices attracted the attention of rogues so that pilfering and illicit working became a serious problem. Miners were undressed and inspected internally on leaving the mine, and armed guards patrolled the site in an attempt to stop people raking through spoil heaps or entering the mine itself.

In 1749 a particularly crafty attempt was made to work the mine illicitly by a man called William Hetherington. He obtained a lease to drive a copper adit on the site and actually found some copper. However, as the workings contained a secret door giving access to the wad mine, Hetherington and friends did quite well for a while. On discovering what was happening the Bankes family cleverly solved the problem by appointing Hetherington as steward – set a thief to catch a thief!

The theft problem became so severe that in 1752, following an armed attack on the mine, an Act was passed in Parliament declaring illegal entry into, or stealing from, a wad mine to be a felony. Punishment for an infringement was a public whipping plus one year's hard labour, or seven years' transportation. Presumably this Act must have been some deterrent but clearly wasn't wholly effective for as late as 1771 there are reports of rogues using gunpowder during the night.

By the late 1830s the proprietors seem to have lost interest in working the mine for themselves, letting it to a succession of mining companies who, by various accounts, didn't do very well. The last one was the Borrowdale Plumbago Mines and Manufacturing Company under the management of Henry Vercoe. This went into liquidation in 1891.

In 1981 under the terms of the will of Mr H. J. R. Bankes, the National Trust was given the family's Kingston Lacy and Corfe Castle estates: included was the Wad Mine. Later a small ceremony took place for the unveiling of a boundary marker at the foot of the fell. This replaced a pre-existing marker (one of several) which was erected in 1752 but destroyed by vandals.

Honister Quarries

An extensive system of underground quarries in the crags and high ground either side of the Honister Pass between Buttermere and Borrowdale. They were last worked by the Buttermere and Westmorland Green Slate Company Ltd, and the material won was an attractive and durable green slate composed of cleaved metamorphosed volcanic ash. Within the site are three distinct quarry locations, Dubs (NY 210135), Yew Crag (NY 224143) and Honister Crag (NY 215140), though only Honister Crag has been worked in recent years. The slate was processed at the Hause (NY 224135) and sold worldwide for roofing, facing, crazy-paving and ornamental work.

Mining Details

There are three slate beds traversing the property, each approximately 40 ft thick and inclined 35° to the horizontal. They are referred to as veins by the quarrymen and will be so described here, though in a strict geological sense the use of this term is incorrect. Between the 'veins' is volcanic rock of no commercial value.

The Quayfoot 'vein' contains a cleaved breccia, which despite several trials, has not proved marketable. Yew Crag vein has been worked on both sides of the Pass; at Yew Crag to the N and at Honister Crag and Dubs to the S. The most recent workings – known as Kimberley Mine – are in this 'vein' and are reached by tunnels at the eastern end of Honister Crag.

On the N side of the pass the Honister vein has hardly been touched, but the southern workings in the face of Honister Crag are truly enormous. The 'vein' has not been worked for some 40 years but under the last company a start was made on connecting the Kimberley and Honister mines.

The normal method of mining was to drive a horizontal tunnel into the 'vein' at outcrop and after a suitable distance open it out by cutting sideways, upward and forward to form a chamber. Slate was obtained by driving the chamber forward, so after a few years the size of the cavity could be considerable. Indeed, an old plan of the Honister 'vein' shows chambers up to 600 ft long, 80 ft wide and 40 ft high with a few pillars of slate left here and there to prevent roof collapse.

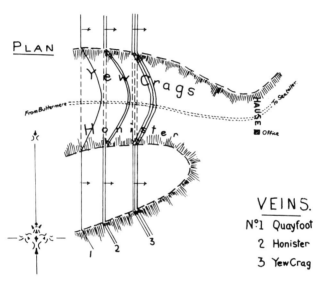

PLAN

VEINS.

Nº1 Quayfoot
2 Honister
3 YewCrag

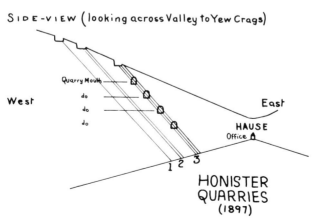

SIDE-VIEW (looking across Valley to Yew Crags)

West

East

HAUSE
Office

HONISTER
QUARRIES
(1897)

As one chamber neared the end of its useful life an adjacent one was started, and quarrymen stated with pride that the population of a major city could be accommodated within the mountain leaving room to spare. Though no exaggeration, any attempt to prove the claim would probably be thwarted, roof collapses having rendered many places inaccessible. Old slate workings are highly unstable and entry should never be attempted.

The course of the slate 'veins' across the crag faces can clearly be seen by the lines of tunnel mouths and surface works associated with pathways and haulage systems.

In the latter part of last century the workings on Honister Crag were connected by external ropeways, but later on underground inclined tramways became the preferred method. The workings on Yew Crag were connected by an external incline and the remains can still be seen. Dubs, the smallest quarry, was linked to the Hause by a tramway whose course on the map was an almost perfect straight line. The bed of this old tramway is now a fell walkers' path, the rails having long since disappeared. Wherever possible these haulage systems were self acting, the weight of descending full wagons hauling up the lighter empty ones.

History

No one is certain when the quarries were first worked or by whom, though according to local legend the latter may well have been a whisky smuggler, named Moses Rigg, operating some 300 years ago, but nothing has ever been found to confirm this. The slate is said, at this time, to have been cut from the highest outcrop on Honister Crag then pony-drawn along an old track (Moses Trod or Sledgate) crossing Dubs Moor, Brandreth and the head of Ennerdale, thence down to Wasdale. Once here transport would have been a relatively easy matter.

The earliest reliable item of information as to tenancy is a lease dated 2nd May 1728 granted to a John Walker enabling him to extract slate at 'Ewecrag and Fleteworth'. The extent of Mr Walker's enterprise is not known nor is that of the other prior to 1879 lease holders. These were: Charles Norman, 30th April 1750; John Atkinson, 14th May 1818; Messrs Jopson and Clark, 28th December 1840; Samuel Wright, 24th November 1848.

What is known, however, is that by 1870 substantial underground workings were in existence at Dubs, Yew Crag and Honister Crag. Slate from the workings was carried in sleds hauled by the quarrymen along treacherous paths. As these paths crossed steep scree slopes and narrow ledges a stumble could result in a man falling hundreds of feet to his death or being run over and crushed by his own sled. The slate was brought down to the Honister Pass road, the empty sled then being towed back for another load.

The extreme physical discomfort of this work is made clear in an account by E. Lynn Linton (1864): 'The noise of the crashing slate comes nearer; now we see the man's eager face; and now we hear his panting breath; and now he draws up by the road side – every muscle strained, every nerve alive, and every pulse throbbing with frightful force. It is a terrible trade – and the men employed in it look wan and worn, as if they were all consumptive or had heart disease'.

Out of these labours came legends; men whose physical achievements were of such magnitude that they were talked of with reverence by succeeding generations. Perhaps the greatest of these was Joseph Clark who according to *Green's Guide to the Lakes* (1819) 'brought down forty-two and a half loads or 10,880 lbs. of slate, from the quarry to the road, in one day; but this was in seventeen journies, averaging each two and a half loads, or 640 lbs. each time, travelling over seventeen miles of the most unfavourable ground, eight miles and a half up hill, with the hurdle, 80 lbs. weight; upon his shoulders. Once but in fewer journies he conducted forty-six loads, or 11,776 lbs. in one day'.

The quarrymen, many of them only going home for a Sunday, lived in small huts scattered about the crags and an example of one of these huts can be seen at Dubs. This is now used by climbers.

In 1870 the quarries were abandoned and nothing more done until 1878 when a company of gentlemen, James Barratt, Alan Salmon and John Sawrey, working slate from high ground near Yew Crag, applied for a lease. They wished to lead their slate down Yew Crag to the road and also to re-open some of the Yew Crag quarries.

The lease was granted on the 28th May 1879 and operations were commenced with great vigour. Within a few months a 230 yard long self-acting tramway had been constructed from the crag to the road and rough barracks erected for workmen. In 1881 the company also acquired the lease to the Honister Crag and Dubs quarries and showed similar vigour in the development of these. The workings in the Honister 'vein' were connected by aerial ropeway to a convenient off-loading point thus eliminating the drudgery of using sleds, but the remoteness of Dubs presented a more difficult problem so in 1886 work was commenced on driving a 800 yard tunnel to link workings in the Honister vein to those at Dubs.

This undertaking promised to be costly (£2,500) but dwindles into insignificance when compared with the tunnel started in 1887 which was to connect the Yew Crag workings with the Newlands Valley (estimated cost £14,000). The roads in those days were poor and it was hoped that a small railway could carry the slate through the tunnel, into and along the Newlands Valley and thence to Braithwaite station on the Cockermouth-Penrith line.

The tunnel to Dubs must have been discontinued for in 1890, it is reported, a tramway from Honister Hause to Dubs was in an advanced stage of construction. Presumably the tramway was a cheaper alternative. Likewise the Newlands Valley tunnel was discontinued, not due to an alternative having been found, but because a landowner – through whose property the railway would have had to pass – refused to co-operate.

Under the new company the quarries went from strength to strength and within a few years were employing 100 men and producing 3,000 tons of slate per year. By 1891 all quarries were either producing or about to do so. However, Dubs proved troublesome; bedeviled by roof collapses and slate discolouration it never yielded really good results right up to its closure in 1932. Around 1895 the company which, almost from its formation, had been called the Buttermere Green Slate Company started to acquire slate quarries in Westmorland, accordingly changing its name to the Buttermere and Westmorland Green Slate Company. Properties were also acquired in north Lancashire but most of these, along with the Westmorland holdings, were eventually given up. Hodge Close quarry, however, was still owned by the company up to its recent closure.

Accommodation for workers was always a problem and in 1893 the construction of eight houses was begun at Seatoller to augment the barracks and scattered huts on the quarry sites.

In 1906 some explorations were made in the Quayfoot 'vein' but results were not encouraging and the trials abandoned. 1907 saw a traction engine replacing horses and taking, daily, 12 ton loads to Keswick each journey. In 1910 rock drills were in use underground.

The 1914-18 war almost brought the quarries to a standstill and this over, it was not easy recruiting new, or regaining past employees. Many had died in action and the survivors, in general, were not so keen to return to such arduous work. Despite the six more houses built at Seatoller in 1918 to attract new recruits the road to recovery was not easy.

The arrival of a new proprietor, Commander Hoare, in 1926 heralded a fresh period of energetic development. Large sheds – the ones to be seen today – were built to accommodate slate splitters and slate dressers, also to house a powerful electric diamond saw used to prepare the blocks prior to splitting. The electricity came from a newly-constructed power house containing a 120 hp engine and dynamo. In 1927 a hostel (now a youth hostel) was built to accommodate some 50 men. This replaced the previous huts and barracks.

Trade went fairly well throughout the depression years, though Dubs was forced to close. The quarries even managed to stay open through part of the Second World War, but were put on a care and maintenance basis only between 1943 and 1945.

In 1960 Leconfield Estates of Cockermouth Castle became the new proprietors and in 1966 Yew Crag quarries closed, having become too unsafe to work. In 1981 the quarries were taken over by Mr B. R. Moore who embarked upon a programme of vigorous development. However, trading conditions were not those anticipated and about 1985 the quarries were closed.

Dale Head Mine

A small copper mine situated below Dalehead Crags. Some ruins are to be seen at NY 222157 and scattered all around them are numerous pieces of vein material spotted with malachite. By following the path up the hill a spoil heap is reached at NY 225155, beside which is a level. A little higher up the fellside is another level which is connected to the lower one by an internal shaft. A little below these workings, in precipitous ground, is a waterfall and at the head of this is another level. The lowest level is not thought to be connected to the other two. No useful historical information has been found.

St. Thomas's Work

An Elizabethan copper working situated near Castlenook (NY 230166). It consists of some openworks on a NE-SW vein.

Salt Well Mines

A group of copper and lead mines. The Salt Well Vein runs from near Park Neb on Derwent Water (NY 255189) to a little S of Manesty and was worked by means of several shafts and levels along its length. About half way along it is intersected by the Brandlehow Lode and some lead was raised in the neighbourhood of the junction.

Black Crag Trial

Just below Black Crag at the top of a scree gully is a shallow openwork (NY 246186). There is supposed to be a very old cross-cut adit driven N for 13 fathoms which cuts the vein under the openwork, but the mouth of the level has not been found. The trial was for lead ore.

Copper Plate Mines

The Copper Plate Vein courses approximately NE-SW and had been worked in the neighbourhood of High Close (NY 246178) and higher up the hillside towards Greenup. It was first wrought in 1566 and again in the mid-1800s. As implied by the name the ores were those of copper.

The level near Greenup (NY 244177) is very old and about 50 ft long. The lower workings at High Close consist of openworks and two levels driven into opposite sides of Ellers Beck. The level driven W is 300 ft long

and clearly very old. The level driven E is 60 ft long and contains a 30 ft deep flooded sump near its entrance. The latter level was driven or re-worked in the 19th century.

Minersputt

An Elizabethan lead working whose precise location has never been established. It is, however, known to be on Skelgill Bank (below Catbells), and accordingly exploited the N or S branch of the Brandlehow Lode. There are some old pit workings on the S branch at NY 244202, and on the N branch is what is now called Old Brandley Mine. Minersputt was one of these, or possibly both.

Driedly Gill Level

A 10 yard long level driven into the S bank of the most northerly branch of Driedly Gill (NY 247098, 2,100 ft contour). This must qualify as the most inaccessible working in the Lake District. There are no signs of mineralisation.

Grains Gill Level

A level and ruined building by the side of a deep ravine (NY 235099). The level is closed and the spoil almost totally devoid of mineralisation. No historical details are known.

Roughtongill Mines
(Roughtongill Mine, Silver Gill Mine, Mexico Mine)

An ancient and very extensive system of mines whose surface workings are scattered about a line drawn from Balliway Rigg (NY 298339) to an old level (NY 309345) in high ground to the E of Clints Gill. Up to 1876 the ores won – in decreasing order of tonnage – were those of lead, copper and zinc. After this and up to the final abandonment in 1894 some small-scale operations were carried out for the extraction of baryte, umber and various mixed mineral clays of use in pigment manufacture.

The mines are justly famous for their many unusual and brightly coloured minerals – mainly decomposition products of primary sulphide ores – and it is still possible, by searching the dumps, to find some good samples. Also the mines are famous for having been very rich; a reputation they do not wholly deserve. The vein system did indeed contain a rich ore body (from which several people made a great deal of money) but this was relatively small compared with the total extent of the workings. A considerable amount of money, too, was lost by others in a search for further rich deposits where they didn't exist.

The three mines are normally grouped under the heading Roughtongill, for they all exploited the same group of veins.

Mining Details

Despite considerable efforts the author has not succeeded in finding a plan for these mines, and – a few partial sketches apart – there is good reason for believing that none was ever made. Fortunately there are still very many company and engineers' reports in existence and by piecing together the information therein, it has been possible, with the aid of 6 in geological maps, to draw a plan which conveys some idea of the work done.

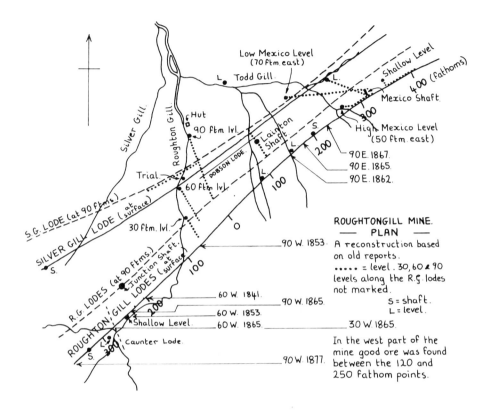

Low Mexico Level
(70 ftm.east)

Shallow Level

400 (fathoms)

Mexico Shaft.

High Mexico Level
(50 ftm.east)

90 E. 1867.
90 E. 1865.
90 E. 1862.

ROUGHTONGILL MINE.
— PLAN —

A reconstruction based
on old reports.
..... = level. 30, 60 ₤ 90
levels along the R.G. lodes
not marked.

S = shaft.
L = level.

90 W. 1853.
90 W. 1865.
30 W. 1865.
90 W. 1877.

60 W. 1841.
60 W. 1853.
60 W. 1865.

In the west part of the
mine good ore was found
between the 120 and
250 fathom points.

Low Mexico Level
Todd Gill.
Silver Gill.
Roughton Gill.
Hut
90 ftm lvl.
Lainton Shaft.
DOBSON LODE.
Trial
60 ftm lvl.
S.G. LODE (at 90 ftms.)
SILVER GILL LODE (at surface)
30 ftm. lvl.
S.
R.G. LODES (at 90 ftms.)
Junction Shaft.
ROUGHTON GILL LODES (surface)
Shallow Level.
Caunter Lode.

From N to S the veins of importance are the Silver Gill Vein, Dobson's Vein, Roughton Gill North Vein and the Great South Roughton Gill Lode.

The Silver Gill Vein was worked from Silver Gill Mine and the deep workings of Roughtongill Mine. Silver Gill Mine is of very early origin and consists of three levels 8, 20 and 50 fathoms below the surface. All are known to be extensive and to have yielded good quantities of lead ore (30 to 60 ozs silver per ton of lead metal) but accurate information is available only on the 50 fathom one. It starts as a 60 fathom long cross-cut to the vein and in 1852 was reported to follow the vein a further 60 fathoms in a westerly direction. At Roughtongill Mine the vein was tried by a short level some 30 ft below the 60 fathom cross-cut portal and from a 100 fathom long level driven from the interior of the 90 fathom cross-cut. It was also tried from deep levels driven off Lainton's Engine Shaft. All explorations from the Roughtongill Mine found the vein poor and uneconomic.

Dobson's Vein, discovered in the 1820s, runs approximately parallel in course and hade to the Silver Gill Vein. It yielded copper ores and was worked from deep levels off the Lainton Engine Shaft. To the W it was seen in the 90 fathom cross-cut but its eastern extent is not known.

The Roughton Gill North Vein and the Great South Lode are shown on geological maps as a single vein. Whether or not they are truly distinct or one monster vein is a topic which caused much heated argument between mining engineers in the 1860s and 70s. The consensus of opinion appears to have had them as distinct veins, but on occasion when cross-cuts were driven from one to find the other nothing was found. This suggests the possibility of one vein incorporating, in places, huge plates of barren rock, known to miners as horses.

The Great South Lode was the richer and was usually 4 ft-8 ft wide, but in places – particularly in the W end of the mine – swelled up to 40 ft. The levels exploiting the two veins meandered from one to the other with many cross-cuts and parallel drives on the way. Frequently the levels ran alongside the veins due to the latter's shattered and collapsible nature and stoping was effected by means of sideways penetrations. In the E end of the mine relatively little ore was found; what there was consisted of decomposition products of lead and copper. A walk along the course of the vein will often turn up samples of such minerals, particularly pyromorphite. The E end was a financial disaster and ruined the company which had spent so much effort in opening it out. The W part, too, was also rather poor except for one rich deposit of galena about 130 fathoms in length. In the neighbourhood of this ore shoot were found smaller amounts of zinc and copper ores.

The North and Great South Lodes were exploited from three main drives,

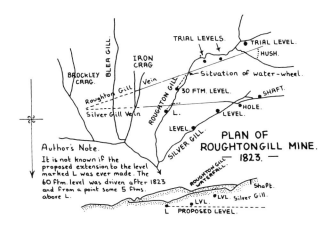

PLAN OF
ROUGHTONGILL MINE.
— 1823. —

Author's Note.
It is not known if the proposed extension to the level marked L was ever made. The 60 ftm. level was driven after 1823 and from a point some 5 ftms. above L.

the 30 fathom, 60 fathom and 90 fathom levels. The mouths of the 60 and 30 are still open and both cross-cuts are clear until the vein is met; roof collapses then bar further progress. The 90 is sealed up and used as a water supply. A shallow level, above the 30, was driven into the W end and the large amount of spoil from it can be seen near the top of the Roughton Gill ravine not far from the remains of a sheepfold. The 90 runs from the extreme W of the mine to about 230 fathoms into the E end, a total distance of 600 fathoms. The 60 and 30 extend a good distance into the W end of the mine but not far into the E end due to falling ground cover.

Lainton's Engine Shaft was sunk from the surface and reached 30 fathoms below the 90. At the confluence of the Thief Gills a caunter lode intersects the Roughton Gill lodes. Near this intersection an internal shaft (Junction Shaft) was sunk from the 90 fathom level to a depth of 20 fathoms and a moderate amount of copper ore extracted from it. At the bottom of the Junction and Lainton shafts the vein had almost died out so the mine was considered exhausted.

In the far E the North and South Lodes were explored from the two Mexico levels and an older level which connects into the Mexico system. All three levels are connected by an internal shaft (Mexico Shaft) which is sunk from the sole of High Mexico Level. There is no connection between Mexico and the 90 E. To the E of Mexico is a shallow level which at the time of writing is still open, but only just. The level on Todd Gill is quite independent of the main vein system and it is said that gold was found here.

History

The Elizabethan company of Mines Royal worked the sett in the latter half of the 16th century, but the few remaining records give little indication of the location of their works or the success of the enterprise. Contemporary examination suggests that most of the work took place near the top of the Silver Gill and Roughton Gill ravines. For example, there is a coffin level near the head of Silver Gill and inspection of the interior of the 30 fathom cross-cut shows it to have been originally a coffin level which was subsequently widened by means of explosives. Nearby are many other, though less conclusive, signs of Elizabethan working. The length of occupation by the Elizabethans is not known but following their departure it would appear that nothing more was done until about 1695.

The next phase of mining was initiated by a Dr Edward Wright, inventor of the reverbatory furnace. Wright's invention revolutionised smelting technique and led to a mining revival throughout England and Wales. Once again little is known of this period and the only informative record to have been found states the following:

Balliway Rigg, in this hill the old man has carried a level through to the Silver Gill and Golden Hue* being near 300 yards, and the wonder is that it should go so far without a shaft for ventilation. There has been great trials in these places but apparently little ore got.

Old man is a term for miners of a bygone era, meaning in this case the Elizabethans. The location of the level mentioned in the report poses something of a problem.

On 24th June 1824, the lease was taken by a seven-man syndicate made up of farmers and miners. One of these was John Dobson after whom the Dobson copper lode was named. After about eight years they ran short of money and were obliged to sell some of their shares. A quarter of these were purchased by a Mr Dickinson who was subsequently instrumental in the driving of the 60 fathom level, the 30 fathom one having been more or less worked out. The 60 was driven W into the rich run of ore and, between 1838 and 1845, 3,200 tons of lead and 150 tons of copper ore were raised. The mine was abandoned when the 21 year lease ran out in 1845.

In 1849† a Mr Henry Compton and another gentleman took the lease and, trading under the name of the Roughtongill Silver Lead and Copper Mining Company, commenced a most vigorous development of the mine. A new smelting works capable of processing 100 tons of lead ore per month was constructed (NY 301362) at a cost of £3,000 and new crushing and dressing machinery erected at the mine. The road down the valley was also greatly improved. The company cleared out the old Silver Gill levels and started the 90 fathom cross-cut and Mexico‡ levels. Between April 1849 and July 1852 nearly £8,000 worth of ore was raised and £6,605 worth sold.

On 1st January 1855 the mine was taken by Messrs James William Dixon and Samuel Merryweather – who, under Compton's ownership, had been the mine manager. Under the new company some 80 tons of ore were extracted per month, and the high Mexico level struck a rich pocket of lead and decomposition minerals; an event which was to trigger the financial ruin of a later company. The proprietors made a good deal of money and in 1863 sold, for £14,000, the mine as a going concern.

Messrs J. J. and J. R. Tustin were the new incumbents and within two years had not only cleared the purchase price but had made a fortune. On 29th April 1865 they in turn sold to a newly-formed organisation, the Caldbeck Fells Consolidated Lead and Copper Mining Company Ltd. By

---

* The name of the highest level on Silver Gill. It is very old and located on the N side of the gill, about 50 ft below the top.

† Messrs George Head Head and John Jameson of the Greenside Company applied for a lease but withdrew at a late hour thus clearing the way for Compton.

‡ The author's theory of how this curious name came about is that it is formed from the 'Me' of Merryweather, the 'i' and 'x' of Dixon and the 'co' of company.

this time most of the rich western deposit had been worked out but this didn't worry the new company too much: some Cornish consulting engineers had told them that the good yields at Mexico were but a minor manifestation of colossal deposits below. Accordingly a huge amount of capital was spent on developing the hitherto barely-touched E end of the mine. The sinking of Lainton's Engine Shaft (James Lainton was the company secretary) was commenced, and the 90 fathom level E was driven forward, striking a respectable run of cerussite (which of course boosted the company's confidence in its decision).

The shaft was a very expensive undertaking costing £25 per fathom to sink (five times the cost of a fathom of level) and necessitating the purchase of a 60 in cylinder steam pumping engine. By mid-1867 the shaft was down to the 90 fathom level and the low Mexico level had reached the Roughton Gill Lode. Unfortunately, by now, the yields from Mexico and from the 90 E had dropped to almost nothing and it soon occurred to the company that its money had been wasted. Accordingly work on the E end was suspended and a very apologetic note sent to the shareholders promising to do better in the future.

Work had, of course, continued in the W end but was more in the nature of scavenging old workings than in any new development. By 1869 the company, getting desperate, was told by a mining engineer, Philip Hawke, that ore could be found by going deeper. The directors enthusiastically took his advice and by early 1870 the engine shaft had been sunk 20 fathoms below the 90 E and the Junction Shaft 10 fathoms below the 90 W. Once again operations at the engine shaft were soon suspended due to heavy running costs (£1,800 per annum) and all effort put into the Junction Shaft.

Following the shutdown of the engine shaft pump, however, the water level in the highly permeable veins rose, flooding the Junction Shaft, and in 1871 a water-powered pump was installed at its head, using water directed down a shaft near the Thief Gills. In 1873 the turbine was replaced by an internal 30 ft water-wheel and this, in 1874, by a 9 hp steam engine.

The story closes with the company, still clinging to the belief that increasing depth would bring riches, continuing to work Junction Shaft with moderate success, and from time to time Lainton's Shaft with no success whatsoever. In 1872 and thereafter problems were exacerbated by a scarcity of miners, many having left for better paid jobs in the collieries of the northeast. By 1876 the company's capital was completely exhausted and it went into liquidation. In eleven years about 3,600 tons of lead ore had been raised, 900 tons of copper ore and 130 tons of blende. On average about 100 men were employed.

Between 1888 and 1894 the Cleator Iron Ore Company worked the mines for baryte, umber and several kinds of clay but these operations were on a fairly small scale involving no important new developments.

In about 1913 the mine was purchased for £15,000 by Carlisle U.D.C. for use as a water supply. At this time the lease was held by Messrs Boehm and Boss (see Carrock Fell Mine), but only for prospecting.

China Clay Mine

A small mine on the Roughton Gill lodes at NY 311347. Although now referred to as the China Clay Mine on OS maps, it was originally called the Hare Stones Umber Mine. It was first worked for umber in 1883 by Messrs Woof and Garth, but operations only lasted one year. The next owner was the Cleator Moor Iron Ore Company which worked it between 1890 and 1894.

In common with other workings on these lodes, this mine contained a large amount of bright white clay, very similar to china clay – hence the name! The amount of umber extracted seems to have been fairly small, but a considerable quantity of white clay must have been removed.

The 1818 Level

The spoil heap of this level may easily be found in a steep-sided gill to the E of the China Clay Mine (NY 315347). The level mouth is harder to find being usually run-over with earth. The level is driven W, is about 50 yards long and its first few feet exhibits a fine example of stone-arching. Near the end, in large and beautifully formed letters, is the inscription:

S R . AGED
1818 : 58

It is not known what mineral the miners were seeking.

Red Gill Mines

(Red Gill Mine, Brae Fell Mine, Wet Smale Gill Trials, Dry Smale Gill Trials

The workings of Red Gill Mine are scattered about the small tongue of land between the confluence of Swinburn Gill and Red Gill (NY 295348). The ores won were those of lead and copper, but the tonnages were never high. Perhaps this mine's greatest claim to fame is as a location of the rare and beautiful blue mineral, linarite, much prized by mineral hunters.

Brae Fell Mine lies about half a mile to the N (NY 298357) and consists of two levels about 10 fathoms apart. The early history of the mine is unknown but it is unlikely that anything worthwhile was ever found within it. The dumps show a small quantity of galena and pyromorphite, and a variety of other secondary minerals in very small amounts.

Roughly half-way between the above are the Wet and Dry Smale Gills where a few shallow trial levels were driven. None of these yielded anything of value.

Mining Details

(i) Red Gill Mine

There are three veins on the property, the main or South Vein being the one on which most of the work was done. This hades to the NE at 1 fathom in 5 and courses 55° W of N through the small tongue of land previously

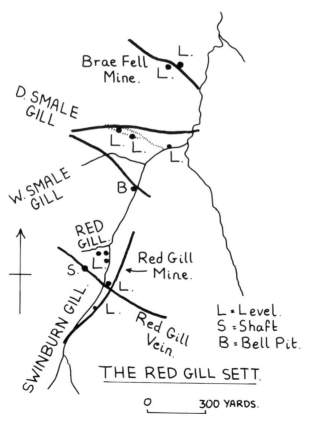

THE RED GILL SETT.

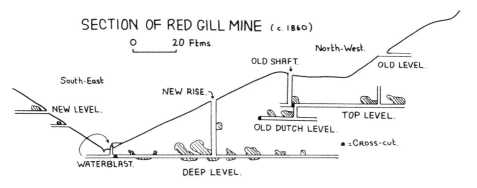

SECTION OF RED GILL MINE (c. 1860)

mentioned. It was worked by a number of short levels and three deep levels known as Top Level, Old Dutch Level and Deep Level, the three latter being reached from short cross-cuts near the confluence of the two gills. From old records it seems that the vein may be two parallel veins a few yards apart, one yielding mainly lead, the other copper, but the available details are vague. Intersecting this vein at right angles is another which follows the course of Swinburn Gill in its upper reaches but diverges from it lower down. This vein has not been explored in any depth. Parallel to the South Vein, and about 500 yards distant, is the North Vein which was tried by means of a bell pit but otherwise not opened up. About 40 fathoms below the deep level cross-cut is another level, started in 1866 when the main workings were given up as a bad job. It was driven N to cut an E-W vein in Dry Smale Gill but whether it got there or not before the company concerned went bankrupt in 1871 is not known.

(ii) Brae Fell Mine

This lies on an approximately NW and SE vein, and was certainly in existence before 1840 but probably not much earlier than that. It was opened several times during the 19th century but without any success.

(iii) Wet and Dry Smale Gills

There is an E-W vein in Dry Smale Gill and a NW and SE vein in Wet Smale Gill. In the late 1860s some pre-existing shallow levels on both the veins were re-opened and a new level driven in Wet Smale Gill. In 1870 a new level was started in Dry Smale Gill. However, closure of the Red Gill Company brought this work to a premature end.

History

The Old Dutch Level in Red Gill Mine is attributed to the Elizabethans, but as the names used by the miners of this era for their many works on the Caldbeck Fells bear no relation to those used in the 19th century and later, it is not possible to be sure.

In the 1820s Red Gill was included in the Roughtongill lease so may have been worked by the syndicate of farmers and miners known to have worked the latter. It was also worked by persons unknown in the 1840s.

In about 1861 the Red Gill Mining Company took the lease to all these mines, erected a water-wheel and dressing apparatus, and commenced extending the old Red Gill workings shown in the section. Up to mid-1866 the Top and Deep levels were driven further NW and connected by a rise from which a short intermediate level was driven. Subsequently because of ventilation problems, another rise was cut connecting the Deep Level with the surface. By late 1865 disappointing results produced a difference of opinion between the directors as to how the mine should be developed further, and mid-1866 saw it resolved in favour of exploring other parts of the sett. Accordingly the old levels in the Smale Gills were re-opened and a new level was driven in Wet Smale Gill.

By late 1866 the company had already lost £3,000 and urgently sought further capital, but take-over negotiations with another company failed when the latter went bankrupt.

In September 1866 a new deep level was commenced 40 fathoms below the Red Gill workings and driven N with the ultimate intent of cutting the Smale Gill veins in depth. Two men were given the job of cleaning out one of the Brae Fell levels also. Work continued with little success until 1871 when the company's funds were completely exhausted. From 1861 to 1871, using a workforce of eight, they succeeded in raising only 25 tons of lead ore and about 45 tons of copper ore.

About 1882 a speculator by the name of Armstrong did a little cleaning up of the Red Gill and Brae Fell mines in the hope of selling them, at good profit, to anyone who might be interested. Nobody was. In about 1902 a Birmingham-based syndicate did a little prospecting work but nothing came of it. In the early 1980s a society of mineralogists applied for permission to open the mine but were refused on safety grounds.

Hay Gill Mines

(Hay Gill Mine, Dale Beck Level, Long Grain Trials, Short Grain Trials, Ingray Gill Trials, Birk Gill Trials, Old Potts Gill Copper Mine)

Hay Gill copper mine is situated near the confluence of the Long and Short Grains of Hay Gill (NY 308360) (grains being an old-fashioned term for branches). Most of the work was done in the late 18th century; a little in

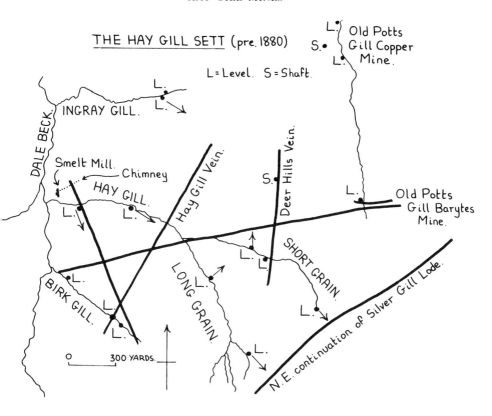

the 1840s. From the early 1840s, Hay Gill Mine was neglected and the lessees put their efforts into exploring other parts of the sett. Accordingly the area is dotted with numerous trial levels, some of which today are very hard to find. They are, with their last date of working:

Dale Beck Level	(NY 303361)	1866
Long Grain Level south	(NY 313353)	1867
Long Grain Level north	(NY 311357)	1866
Short Grain Level north	(NY 306368)	1870
Short Grain Level middle	(NY 313358)	1873
Short Grain Level south	(NY 315358)	pre-1860
Ingray Gill Level north	(NY 317355)	1869
Ingray Gill Level south	(opposite N level)	1871
Ingray Gill Level middle	(NY 306368)	?
Birk Gill Level west	(NY 302357)	?
Birk Gill Level middle	(NY 305354)	One of these worked in
Birk Gill Level east	(adjacent to middle level)	1861 but not known which.

None was particularly successful. The veins concerned yielded small amounts of lead and copper ores.

Old Potts Gill Copper Mine consists of two levels and a shaft located on the W side of the lower reaches of what was in those days called Priestman Gill, or alternatively Man Gill, but nowadays is known as Gill Beck (NY 318371). The ores were those of lead and copper but the mine was not a success. Work started in 1867 and finished in 1871. The lower level is now used as a water supply.

Mining Details

The workings and vein locations are shown on the vein plan and, where known, a small arrow points from the level to the vein concerned.

The extent of the stopes in Hay Gill Mine is not known, but it would seem

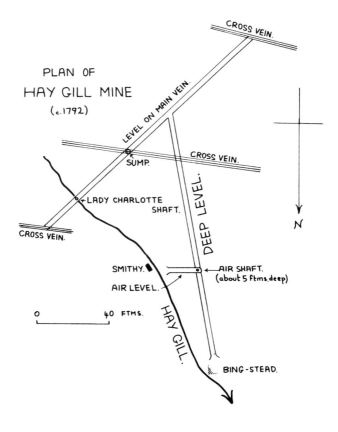

PLAN OF
HAY GILL MINE
(c.1792)

that the small amount of ore there was very rich. As very little work was done after the mid-1790s, other than brief cleaning out and inspection, the plan should be a good representation of the total extent of the workings.

No plan of Old Potts Gill Copper Mine has been located and old reports are too vague to allow a reconstruction. It would appear that the high level, driven in a westerly direction, struck a N-S vein. Levels were driven off N and S and the main one continued W meeting several ore-bearing strings along which further exploratory levels were driven. The low level ran approximately SSW to intersect the N-S vein under its point of intersection with the high one. The spoil heaps are quite large, each one indicating about 300-400 yards of driving.

History

Almost all the historical information concerning Hay Gill Mine comes from the 'Bargain Book of Jos. Scott'. These are the entries:

20 July 1785. Agreed to sink in wet sump, 2 fathoms at £6 6s. 0d. per fathom.

26 July 1785. To drive the low level to unwater said sump.

October 1786. A short level driven for air joined the deep level by a sump of 5 fathoms.

2 February 1788. The vein was cut, 9 ft wide.

4 December 1788. Wet sump reached. This sump was from an old level on the course of the vein set in the beck and 14 fathoms higher.

18 November 1790. Bargain agreed for cutting a wheel case.

25 June 1792. Bargain for driving the low level to the south-west.

On 1st July 1839, the mine was leased by a large syndicate of gentlemen calling themselves the Hay Gill Mining Company. Their initial intent, soon dismissed, was to work Hay Gill mine at a deeper level, but the driving of a new deep adit would have been a lengthy and costly business and if worked from Lady Charlotte Pit would have necessitated the installation of a particularly powerful water-wheel. However, absence of a sufficiently high flow of locally available water precluded anything further ever being done with the mine.

Either this or another company worked the western part of the sett up to mid-1862 and then abandoned it. In June 1866 W. J. Vercoe's East Cumberland Mining Company leased the sett but stopped work for want of success in about April 1874, after raising some 7 tons of lead and 15 tons of copper ores.

Dry Gill Mine

A fairly small lead mine near the intersection of the Dry Gills (NY 325346) and famous as a source of the rare mineral campylite, small samples of which may still be found in the dumps. The last major work was done in 1869, though a little exploration took place as late as 1894.

Mining Details

The Dry Gill Vein is believed to be the western continuation of the Carrock End Copper Lode. It courses approximately E-W, hades N at about 1 fathom in 6 and is reported to have been up to 6 yards in width. Intersecting the vein almost at right angles are the probable continuations of the Carrock Tungsten Mine veins,* each of which shifts the Dry Gill Vein by a few yards.

The deep or Pattinson level is open, situated at NY 325346, and was driven W on the course of the vein. Further upstream on the steep N side of the cutting is the spoil heap of a northerly driven cross-cut to the vein (NY 322345). The mouth of the cross-cut is obscured by a heavy cover of landslip material. By climbing up the bank of the gill from the spoil heap to grass a shaft and subsidence hole can be found on the back of the vein.

Between the two levels, on the S side of the gill and opposite a ruined sheepfold, is another level (open) driven S. This is not connected with Dry Gill Vein but was a small trial on a N-S copper-bearing vein.

A little galena was found by internal cross-cuts driven into the N-S veins, but in the Dry Gill Vein itself the mineral content was a complicated mix of sand, clay, iron oxide, baryte, psilomelane, pyromorphite and campylite: difficult to process and therefore commercially unattractive.

As no plan can be found it is, unfortunately, not possible to make much sense of the large number of records still in existence.

In 1868 a level (NY 345346) was driven some 30 or 40 fathoms in order to try the vein in the hitherto unexplored E ground but work was abandoned when the vein proved barren.

The mine was never a success: tonnages were small and the high arsenic content of the ores caused problems in smelting. It would seem, however, that small quantities of the coloured ores were sold to glass manufacturers.

History

The mine, relatively speaking, is not that old and was certainly not worked prior to 1820. On 1st November 1846 the lease was taken by Hugh Lee Pattinson, a chemical manufacturer from Washington House near Gateshead and the inventor of a famous lead refining process. He worked the mine for about six years and raised between 120 and 300 tons of coloured lead ores.

* Not tungsten bearing here.

In 1859 the mine was taken by F. W. Emerson and C. E. Symonds, trading as 'The Dry Gills and Stone Ends Mining and Smelting Company Ltd', but they appear to have had little success, selling the mine in 1863 to Messrs John and Jesse Tustin, the lessees of Roughtongill Mine. The Tustin's employed six men in the mine essentially for prospecting rather than proper working. The existing levels were driven further W and a little trenching done to determine the position of the vein in the E, also a smithy and office were built. Very little ore was removed.

In 1865 Dry Gill, Carrock End and Roughtongill mines were sold to the Caldbeck Fells Consolidated Lead and Copper Mining Company Ltd. The same six men continued the western driving of the levels and made a number of internal and external exploratory cross-cuts. No good ore was found and in 1869 work ceased.

The Cleator Iron Ore Company which worked Potts Gill Barytes Mine and Roughtongill for baryte and umber (1888-1894) showed some interest in Dry Gill Mine but probably did no more than a little cleaning out and prospecting.

Carrock End Mine

An old copper mine at the foot of the steep eastern face of Carrock Fell. The workings are to be found in the neighbourhood of NY 351343 and consist of four cross-cut levels, a hush and the scant remains of a shaft. The last work was done in December 1869.

Mining Details

The Carrock End Vein runs along the foot of Carrock Fell on a course approximately 25° W of N. Very near Stone Ends Farm it crosses under the Mosedale road and at approximately NY 351343 swings sharply W into the hillside ultimately re-appearing, it is thought, at Dry Gill Mine as the Dry Gill Vein. The hade is about 1 fathom in 6 to the E. The main ore was probably copper pyrite.

Mining here was never on a large scale, the most ambitious works being in about 1840 when a 24 fathom shaft was sunk. The ground in this neighbourhood is very wet and the shaft had to be drained by a particularly powerful wheel, water for which had to be most expensively brought by a leat from Carrock Beck. The cross-cuts were exploratory drives and do not lead to any substantial inner workings.

History

The earliest record of what is probably Carrock End Mine is found in an old report, c. 1700 and quoted below, on the Caldbeck Mines. Although the identification is not positive a study of some very old maps suggests it to be correct:

> Dutch Moss vein lies south west and has been wrought for about 300 yards in length, the shafts and opencasts being about 30 or 40 yards between. There has a level been begun that would have been 9 or 10 fathoms under the old mans working but it was never got up to that work. There has been also a gin and a great deal done for taking off the water which seems to us that they have had some encouragement in working the shafts above.

The 1790s saw it worked by William Roe and Thomas Smyth, lessees of Driggith Mine, but other than the occasional small pocket of ore nothing was found.

In 1839 the lease was taken by the Revd Francis Thompson who, using a workforce of 20 men, sank a shaft to a depth of 24 fathoms. Cross-cuts were driven to the vein at the 13 and 23 fathom levels and, up to the mine's abandonment in 1842, 70 tons of copper ore was raised.

Between 1863 and 1865 the lease was held by Messrs J. J. and J. R. Tustin who in 1863 started on some unrewarding exploratory work and gave up a year later. In April 1865 the Tustins sold this concern, also Dry Gill and Roughtongill mines, to the Caldbeck Fells Consolidated Lead and Copper Mining Company Ltd. Between March and December 1869 a few men were put to re-timbering one of the old levels, after which nothing further was done.

Driggith Mine

This large mine was worked primarily for lead but small amounts of copper and baryte were also raised from time to time. The early workings were at the head of Driggith Beck and consisted of a number of shafts, openworks and levels. Two of these levels were open as late as 1940, the 30 fathom level at NY 327353 and the No 12 at NY 324353.

The later deep workings are situated at what is termed the Sandbeds end of the mine and consist of two levels; the 60 fathom at NY 330359 and 90 fathom at NY 331362. The latter was used, in 1956, as an access level to the Sandbeds West Barytes Mine. The last major work here was done in 1874, since when there have been a number of unsuccessful attempts to re-open, the last being in 1948.

Mining Details

There are several veins in the sett, but only two are worthy of note – the Driggith Main Vein which is the NE continuation of the Roughton Gill lode, and the less important South Vein which runs parallel to it. The course of the former is well approximated by drawing a line from NY 320350 to NY 330360.

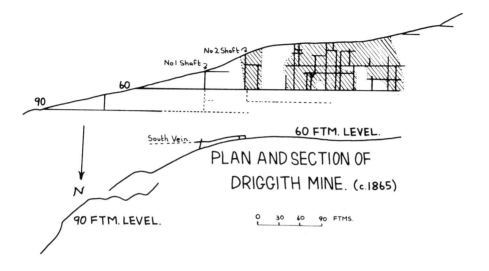

PLAN AND SECTION OF DRIGGITH MINE. (c.1865)

Not unexpectedly the vein here, as at Roughtongill, contained a large number of minerals, primary and decomposition products of lead and copper, blende and baryte. Also, in common with Roughtongill, the mine was rich near the surface but poor in depth. The very long 90 fathom level of Driggith was effectively barren over its entire length. Once again, as the first arrivals made a great deal of money, so the latecomers lost much.

Very high silver content has been claimed (but is suspect) for the lead in this mine – up to 60 ozs per ton of lead metal.

History

The mine's working is supposed to have been initiated by the Lord of the Manor, who, owing to his lack of knowledge in the art of smelting, sustained great financial loss and abandoned it. Unfortunately, the account that gives this information does not quote a date.

In 1791 a lease was taken by Messrs William Roe and Thomas Smyth of Liverpool who worked the mine to a depth of 30 fathoms and also erected a small smelting works by the side of Carrock Beck (NY 352350). No details of the tonnages produced are available but the pair are reported to have done very well out of the venture.

In 1810 Messrs Richardson and Lowrey, two Carlisle gentlemen, took over. With a workforce of about forty they raised 200 tons of lead ore per year until selling out in 1822. Like their predecessors they profited well.

The next purchaser was Thomas Bradyll of Conishead Priory near Ulverston, and henceforth the prosperity of the mine declined. Bradyll drove the 60 fathom level from Sandbeds but by 1834 the cost of this long and unproductive drive had exhausted his resources. Messrs Barratt and Bennett acquired the mine in 1836 and in 1840 sold it to Messrs Dickinson and Company whose mounting losses also forced the stoppage of work in 1849.

For the next few years the mine stood idle until leased by Messrs George Brocklebank and William Jeffrey. They drove the 60 fathom level forward and found a good run of ore coming down from the 30, which fact returned the mine to a reasonably prosperous state. However, much of this gain was offset by the heavy cost of the 90 fathom level started in 1859. As a result of surveying errors and the partners being led astray in pursuance of false veins, this tortuous level did not reach the main vein, near the foot of No 1 shaft, until 1867.

On 25th March 1865 the mine was purchased for £18,750 by the West Cumberland Silver Lead Mining Company Ltd which retained Jeffrey as its manager. Things went wrong from the start as operations were hindered by a shortage of miners. There were, too, severe problems with water, not removed until the 90 hit the vein and unwatered it. The 30 fathom level was driven forward hitting disordered barren ground, and although a new internal 75 fathom level struck a good run of galena it was so intermingled with blende that the dressing plant could not handle it.

Meanwhile the SW continuation of the 90 fathom level never came upon anything of value. Consequently an average of only 100 tons of ore per year were raised and most of this from scavenging old workings. Short exploratory cross-cuts were driven to the South Vein but these also proved worthless. By 1874 the company had run out of money, all work stopped, and on 7th October of that year all the plant and machinery was auctioned.

In 1905, one E. F. Goodall cleaned out the 30 fathom and No. 12 levels, but sold little ore because of the problems in separating the baryte/galena/blende mix. Work stopped in 1907. In 1926 J. H. Clay, who was at the time working Potts Gill Baryte Mine, attempted to clear out the 30 and 60 fathom levels, but the job proved too difficult through blockages caused by collapsed deads, so he quickly gave up.

In 1943 Messrs T. and W. T. Shaw partly explored the 12 and 30 levels but transferred the lease, in 1944, to a Mr E. Gregory who raised some baryte and in turn sold his interests, in 1948, to McKechnie Brothers of Widnes. They too attempted to work some of the old stopes in the 30 fathom level but experienced the same problems as did J. H. Clay and soon abandoned the venture.

The Caldbeck Fells Barytes Mines

(Old Potts Gill, East Potts Gill, Sandbeds East, Sandbeds West, Deer Hills)

With the exception of Old Potts Gill, all these mines date from the 1940s and were finally abandoned in 1966. The Old Potts Gill baryte veins are located at the head of Gill Beck, or Priestman Gill as it used to be known, and the early workings were shallow levels on their outcrop (NY 320361), the deepest being No 1 at 1,484 ft A.O.D. The later deep workings were accessed by the Endeavour cross-cut adit (NY 320365) at 1,319 ft A.O.D.

East Potts Gill Mine was the result of a successful exploration of the far eastern part of the old mine. The initial workings were from levels in the neighbourhood of NY 321361 but later a deep cross-cut was driven from a point adjacent to the Endeavour Level mouth

Sandbeds East Mine was accessed from a 90 fathom cross-cut (NY 333362) and a level in Blea Gill (NY 337359). Further to the E a level, called the Howthwaite Level, was driven from NY 340358 but this was only in the nature of an exploration and did not go under the main workings. Sandbeds West Mine was accessed from the old 90 fathom level of Driggith Mine (NY 331362) and also by 67, 60, 50, 40 and 30 fathoms levels driven W on the course of the vein.

The excavations at Deer Hills were simply trials. A short level was driven from NY 310365, and two others from NY 313365 and NY 314363. The latter two are connected by an internal rise.

The total output of this group was 140,000 tons of baryte.

History and Mining Details

The plan of the sett has been constructed from a survey of the site and from the very detailed numerical information given in W. T. Shaw's *Mining in the Lake Counties*. The letters in brackets, below, refer to the level mouths as labelled on the plan.

(i) Old Potts Gill

There are two veins, the N which proved the most productive, and the S. Both veins hade S at about 1 fathom in 2 and the filling was crushed and rotten rock containing ribs of baryte.

The two baryte veins have been known about for a very long time, certainly since the beginning of the 19th century. In 1871 under W. J. Vercoe's East Cumberland Company (see Hay Gill Mine), two men were put to exploring the outcrop by means of shallow levels. Baryte at that time had little market, and the hope was that a little deeper down this would be replaced by quartz, more conducive to the presence of lead and copper. Work was stopped in 1874 when the company failed.

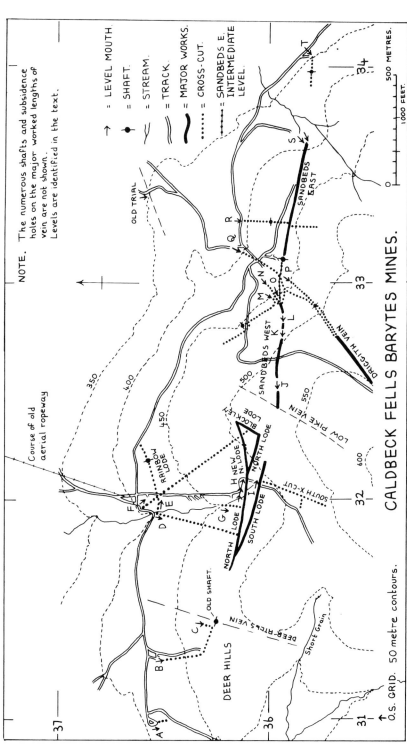

NOTE. The numerous shafts and subsidence holes on the major worked lengths of vein are not shown. Levels are identified in the text.

→ = LEVEL MOUTH.
● = SHAFT.
≈ = STREAM.
= TRACK.
━ = MAJOR WORKS.
⋯ = CROSS-CUT.
⋯⋯ = SANDBEDS E. INTERMEDIATE LEVEL.

CALDBECK FELLS BARYTES MINES.

Course of old aerial ropeway

O.S. GRID. 50 metre contours.

DEER HILLS

DEER-RTLES VEIN

Short Grain

OLD SHAFT.

NORTH LODE

SOUTH LODE

BLOCKLEY LODE

H NEW N. LODE

NORTH LODE

SOUTH X-CUT.

RAINBOW LODE

OLD TRIAL

SANDBEDS WEST

SANDBEDS WEST VEIN

LOW PIKE VEIN

DRIGGITH VEIN

SANDBEDS EAST

0   500 METRES.
0   1000 FEET.

Based upon the 1974 Ordnance Survey 1:10,000 map with permission of the Controller of Her Majesty's Stationery Office, Crown Copyright reserved.

SECTIONS OF POTTS GHYLL MINE

Between 1888 and 1892 the operator was the Cleator Moor Iron Company which also worked Roughtongill, and during this time some 500 tons of baryte were raised.

In 1914 the mine was taken by a Mr Goodall, but in 1915 the lease was assigned to one Mr F. J. Ryland who conducted affairs under the name of the Potts Gill Baryte Mining Company. He worked it from 1915 to 1920 achieving an output of 3,000 tons, but in 1920 a fall in the price of baryte closed the mine and by 1921 Ryland was bankrupt.

In 1926 it was re-opened by J. H. Clay's Caldbeck Mining Company but only worked intermittently, producing 4,800 tons of baryte in 1927-31 and 5,100 tons in 1938-40. By 1928 it became necessary to go below No 1 level (G) and so the Endeavour deep adit level (D) was started, but was stopped shortly afterwards through lack of funds. 1936 saw it re-started and 1938 completed.

The mine was purchased in 1940 by McKechnie Brothers of Widnes, as were all the other mines in this group. In 1942, as a result of manganese contamination, the west started to give trouble, but the rest of the mine was worked from the deep level until 1947.

(ii) East Potts Gill

This can be considered as exploiting the last 510 ft of the North (or Main) Lode and the triangular shaped vein system to which it is attached. The point of attachment is intersected by a NNE fault called Shaw's Cross-course.

In about 1942 a level, called the Jon Level, (1,594 ft A.O.D.) (H), was driven E along the course of the N Lode and at about 130 ft from the entrance intersected the hitherto unknown New North Lode. This was driven on for 780 ft and in turn the Blockley Lode was discovered. The New North Lode yielded good baryte over most of its length and the Blockley Lode was productive for 360 ft of the 500 ft length driven. In order to get deeper another two levels were driven E along the North Lode, the Victory Level (1,564 ft A.O.D.) (H), which runs 310 ft before meeting Shaw's Cross-course and the Gill Level (1,520 ft A.O.D.) (H) which runs 510 ft before meeting the cross-course. That part of the North Lode belonging to the triangle was generally poor. In 1946 the deep cross-cut adit (1,319 ft A O.D.) (F) was driven to get under these workings and at a few feet in from the entrance intersected the Rainbow Lode. The latter was explored (E) but turned out to be of no value.

The South Lode was explored from the Thomas Level (I) which is driven E and at about 50 ft in meets the southern continuation of Shaw's Cross-course. The level was driven 450 ft beyond the cross-course but the quality of the vein was poor. A 1,030 ft long cross-cut was driven S from the Thomas Level with the intention of locating other lodes, but nothing of much value was found.

The Old and East mines yielded a total of 90,000 tons of baryte.

(iii) Sandbeds East

The vein was discovered in 1927 but not worked until 1946. A 90 fathom cross-cut (R) was driven 870 ft S and intersected the vein 160 ft below surface. The level was continued E along the vein for 1,060 ft until it hit the surface in Blea Gill: most of this distance was stoped. The same level was also driven some 700 ft W of the cross-cut but the ground here was poor. Above the 90 is an internal 80 fathom level.

A 100 fathom level (S) was driven W from Blea Gill to get under the 90 workings. The total length driven was 1,780 ft of which 870 ft was stoped. At about the 85 fathom horizon an internal intermediate level was driven W and this intersected the Sandbeds West Vein. The Howthwaite Level (T) yielded nothing of value.

The yield of Sandbeds East was relatively poor – 16,964 tons.

(iv) Sandbeds West

In 1952 a 60 fathom level (M) was driven at the same horizon as, and NW of, the Driggith 60 fathom level (P) but nothing was found and the work was given up. In 1956, however, the Sandbeds East intermediate level struck the Sandbeds West Vein enabling the latter's position to be located. Accordingly the 60 fathom level was re-started and turned S to intersect the new vein. The mine was subsequently opened out by other levels and the details of ground worked are given below:

90 fathom (Q), length 600 ft – not much work done.
67 fathom (N), length 420 ft – ?
60 fathom (M), length 1,130 ft – 570 ft stoped.
50 fathom (O), length 1,370 ft – 760 ft stoped.
40 fathom (L), length 1,350 ft – 850 ft stoped.
30 fathom (K), length 1,100 ft – 650 ft stoped.

The 67 level terminates, to the E, in a stope on the Sandbeds East intermediate level. This is the only connection between the East and West mines. The 90 Sandbeds West Level was accessed from the old 90 fathom Driggith Level (Q) at a point where it leaves the Sandbeds West Vein.

At about 120 ft in from the mouth of the 60 an exploratory cross-cut was driven N but nothing of value was found. At the W end of the vein is an old level (J). There are numerous old trials along the nearby Low Pike Vein. The yield of the mine was 35,000 tons of baryte.

(v) Deer Hill Trials

These were made about 1961 but did not locate any useful veins (A, B, C).

Carrock Fell Mines

(Carrock Tungsten Mine, Upper Brandy Gill Mine)

The major and most evident working within the sett is the tungsten mine. It is situated at the confluence of Grainsgill Beck and Brandy Gill (NY 324329) and is the only location, outside Cornwall, at which tungsten has been mined in this country. It has been worked a number of times since the 1850s but never for very long, being viable only when the price of tungsten is particularly high. The last work was in October 1981.

Prior to the beginning of the 20th century, there was little interest in tungsten and although some was mined, the sett was worked mainly for lead and copper. These workings were very small and most are now lost under the spoil of the tungsten mine. One however, may still be found, Upper Brandy Gill Mine, (NY 322338). It exploited a small E-W vein and was abandoned in about 1870.

The lead and copper works are of little consequence and had finished by 1900. Unless otherwise stated the rest of the discussion refers only to the tungsten mine, or simply 'the mine'.

Mining Details

There are five veins of importance, these being the Smith, Harding, Emerson, Wilson and Waterfall veins.

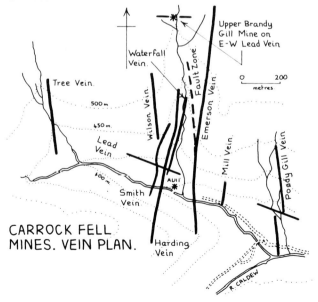

CARROCK FELL MINES. VEIN PLAN.

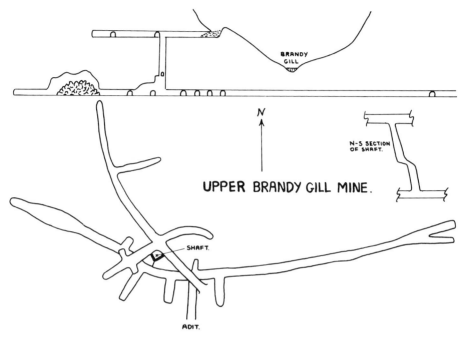

UPPER BRANDY GILL MINE.

The Emerson Vein was the first to be worked to any extent and is named after F. W. Emerson, the first major lessee of the sett. South of the beck the vein appears to be barren, but a good amount of wolframite was found to the N. The old workings are long abandoned and the modern plan refers to the Emerson Vein exploration which was an attempt to locate the vein in new ground.

The Harding Vein has been by far the most productive, yielding wolframite and scheelite. South of the beck the old stopes have since been used as a dump for mill fines sludge, all the ore having been worked out – most of it long ago by the early adventurers. However, to the N it was productive right up to the mine's recent closure and it is expected that driving forward may well expose further deposits.

The early workings on the Smith Vein were for arsenopyrite, and prior to the First World War the mine did a small but flourishing trade in arsenic. However, much of the driving on this vein is quite recent. The Smith Vein South contains very little tungsten ore, but wolframite and scheelite have been found in reasonable quantities in the North Vein.

The Wilson and Waterfall Veins, along with the new Emerson working, have merely been the subject of prospecting.

Continuation of the workings to the N could reveal further deposits of ore. It is also thought that there may be substantial deposits below adit but

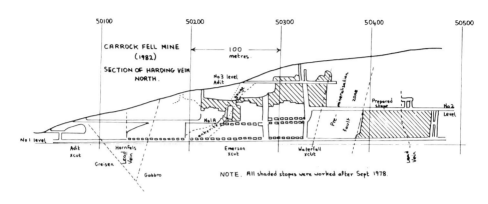

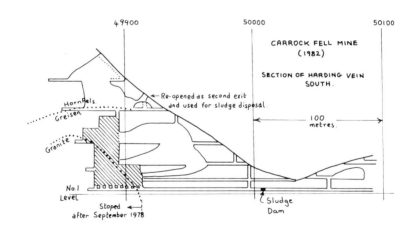

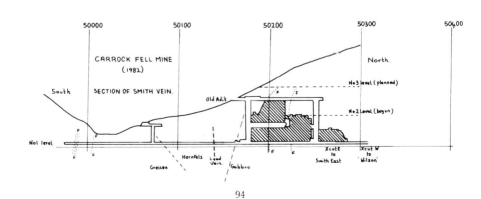

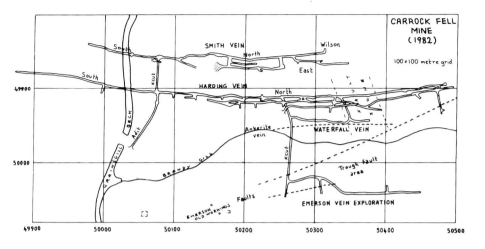

exploitation of these would require a new deep adit to unwater the mine. The proportion of tungsten ore to gangue in these veins is very small, typically 1% (calculated as WO_3).

History

There is a record of a little lead and copper mining having taken place in the Brandy Gill area sometime in the 16th century and Brandy Gill Mine itself was being worked *c.* 1724 by one Thomas Hillary.

In 1852, F. W. Emerson of the Trereife Chemical Works, Penzance, started work. As with his predecessors his interest was not in tungsten but in copper and lead, for even at that time tungsten was little more than a laboratory curiosity. The copper was worked from Brandy Gill Mine and lead from the E-W vein near the foot of the Gill. By 1854 the road to the mines had been constructed, but operations were soon stopped by a wrangle over mineral rights. The records are rather vague on this point but it would appear that one landowner held the rights to lead and copper and another held the same to other metals. Unfortunately for Emerson, his lease was with the wrong person so he was compelled to abandon his lead and copper works. Accordingly he put his efforts into one of the tungsten veins, the one now named after him.

No further details are available until 1863 when the mines were taken by Messrs Leicester and Hutchinson as a sub-let from Emerson who renewed his lease in 1864. In 1872 the company name was changed to M. Hutchinson and Company and work continued until 1877. There is only one record of production during these years: $5\frac{1}{2}$ tons of lead in 1874.

In 1902 a prospecting licence was granted to James Harding of Penrith, who seems to have stayed until 1905 operating under the name of Carrock Mines Ltd. The only information about this work shows it to have been on a very small scale.

In 1906 the mine was taken by two Germans, William Boss and Frederick Boehm, calling themselves the Cumbrian Mining Company Ltd. It is not surprising that Germans should have taken an interest in the mine, for the value of tungsten in armaments manufacture was much better appreciated in that country than in this. By 1914 the Germans had a highly efficient and productive arms industry, much of this a direct result of the use of tungsten high speed steel and tungsten cutting tools. It is a sad fact that much of this tungsten came from the Cornish tin mines where it was regarded as a useless by-product. The German company stopped work in 1912.

The mine was re-opened in 1913 by the Carrock Syndicate, a group of steel manufacturers, and was run by Anthony Wilson (see also Thornthwaite and Threlkeld Mines). The venture was also partially financed by the Government. During the five year occupancy 13,911 tons of ore were mined and 10,116 tons milled yielding 75 tons WO_3 content, but at the war's end the demand – and therefore the price – fell and the mine closed.

The 27th January 1917 edition of the magazine *Autocar* carried a short article on the mine and told an amusing story. It would appear that a geologist was sent by the Geological Survey to explore the property for further tungsten veins and, because of the secret nature of his work, couldn't and wouldn't explain to the locals what he was doing. As the country was in the grips of a German spy mania at this time, it seemed not unlikely to the local population that they had a spy on their hands. When one day the visitor was observed digging a hole in the vicinity of the mine, this was all the verification they needed. A posse of locals crept up behind and overpowered him, took his tools and notebooks, dealt out what might be called a little rough treatment and locked him up in a local school-house pending the arrival of the police. Next morning the latter put matters right.

No further work was done here until 1942 when the capture of Burma created a tungsten shortage, prompting the Ministry of Supply to re-open the mine. Using Canadian Servicemen experienced in hard rock mining, they drove the old levels forward connecting the workings by a cross-cut – still the main entrance to the mine. 2,500 ft of development was done on the Harding Vein, and 1,500 ft on the Smith Vein, and an estimate made of the recoverable ore reserves. No ore, however, was mined, for by the end of the explorations in 1943 the supply of imported tungsten had improved and the mine closed.

In the early 1950s the Korean War cut off an important world source of tungsten and the price shot up. A company called Durham Chemical was eager to take advantage of the situation, but as the mine lay within the boundary of the then proposed National Park, its application to mine ran into a number of obstacles, only resolved in 1953. By this time the price had dropped again.

In 1971 the WECO Development Corporation of Denver, Colorado, leased the mine through its U.K. subsidiary, World Wide Energy (U.K.) Ltd. £250,000 was spent on a new mill and a little underground development. Between June 1971 and July 1972 the price of ore concentrates dropped by 33% and work was stopped. From 1972 to 1976 the mine was held on a care and maintenance basis. In 1976, WECO granted the Carrock Fell Mining Company Ltd, a subsidiary of Amalgamated Industrials, a one year lease of the mine with an option to enter into a joint venture at the end of this period. By April 1977 the mine was brought into production and, in the same year, the joint venture option was exercised.

The mill throughput rose to a steady level of 50 tons a day the mine becoming profitable during the first six months of 1978, the year the Carrock Fell Mining Company was purchased by the National Carbonising Company Ltd. Mining continued and a great deal of exploratory work was done, but the continued depressed state of the tungsten market caused work to cease in October 1981. The mine, once again, was put on a care and maintenance basis and in the autumn of 1982 sold to Minworth of Derbyshire. At the time of writing the mine and plant is once more on a care and maintenance basis.

Little Wiley Gill Mine

A 40 yard long level located a few feet NE of the confluence of Red Gill and Little Wiley Gill (NY 297322). There is no significant presence of any ore mineral but some highly attractive clusters of quartz crystals have been found here.

Bannerdale Mine

A group of small workings located on Bannerdale Crags near Mungrisedale. The lead workings are to be found in the neighbourhood of NY 335295 and exploited an E-W vein system containing galena with smaller amounts of blende in a matrix of quartz, baryte and smashed country-rock. The low level is about 150 ft long and higher up the hill is an openwork. At the end of this openwork is another level which is about 100 ft long and has been stoped to a height of about 12 ft over most of its length. Higher still can be found a small trial – little more than a scratching on the vein.

Not far from the above is the so-called graphite level (NY 336293). The graphite is said to have occurred in small lumps at the edges of the quartz vein, some being supposed, at one time, to have been used in the making of pencils. The level is very small however, and couldn't have yielded much.

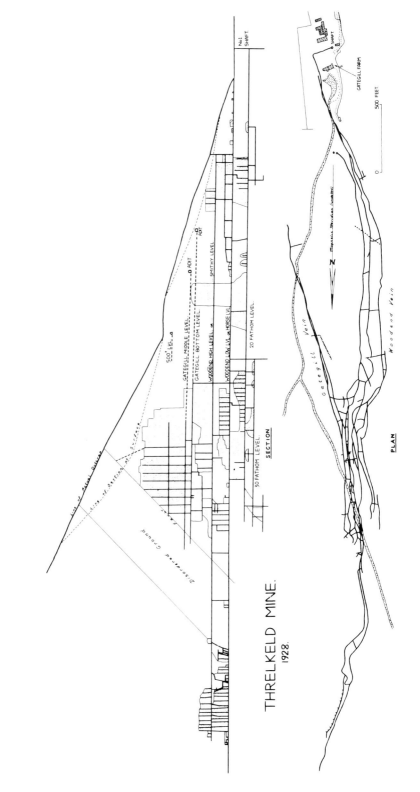

THRELKELD MINE.
1928.

SECTION

PLAN

No.1 SHAFT

ADIT
ADIT
500' LVL.
GATEGILL MIDDLE LEVEL.
GATEGILL BOTTOM LEVEL.
WOODEND HIGH LEVEL.
SMITHY LEVEL.
WOODEND LOW LVL. or HORSE LVL.
20 FATHOM LEVEL.
30 FATHOM LEVEL.

Line of Section on Plan.
Limit of actual Working.
Disordered Ground.
FAULT.

SHAFT
GATEGILL FARM

N

Gategill Vein
Woodend Vein
Magnetic Meridian (variable)

0   500 FEET

Official statistics show seven tons of lead ore to have been raised in 1854, and a trial is supposed to have been made by a Mr Crozier around the year 1870.

Saddleback Old Mine

The mine consists of two widely-separated workings. The higher working is situated about 500 yards NE of Scales Tarn (NY 332286) and the lower, a level reputedly 400 yards long, is situated high up Mousthwaite Comb (NY 344276). Both are believed to lie on the same vein.

The opening of the mine was with the intention of finding lead, but the vein filling consisted almost entirely of dark brown/orange limonite, so much so that an attempt was made in the 1890s to sell it for use as a pigment. The scheme proved impracticable.

Ownership of this mine is uncertain. According to official mineral statistics the proprietor from 1874 to 1876 was the Saddlebeck Mining Company. However, this company owned Threlkeld Mine at the time and there is nothing in the company reports to suggest it to have run this mine as well. In 1894, the mine was held by the Long Meg Plaster Company, but nothing further is known.

Threlkeld Mine

A large lead and zinc mine situated at the foot of Hall's Fell (NY 325261). The early history of the mine is obscure but from 1879 to 1928 it was highly productive surviving the catastrophic fall, around 1921, in the price of zinc which closed Thornthwaite and Force Crag. The mine is certainly not exhausted and a short time ago rumours were abroad that someone was interested in re-opening.

Mining Details

There are two veins of importance, the Woodend Vein and the Gategill Vein. The Gategill was the earlier to have been worked but the Woodend was worked the more. The former yielded mainly galena; the latter was rich in galena, blende and iron pyrite, and the richest part of the mine was where the veins intersected. The workings below the Woodend Low Level were plagued in later years by large volumes of water.

The Gategill workings date back to at least the 17th century, and in the 1820s mining engineer John Taylor had some involvement with the mine. In 1848 Messrs Walton and Cowper, the owners of Force Crag Mine, took a lease working the mine up to 1863.

In 1874 a local syndicate formed the Saddlebeck Mining Company Ltd and worked both veins but by 1877 ran into a serious cash shortage and general lack of support from shareholders. In 1879 the company was on the threshold of abandoning the mine when William Bawden (manager of Coniston Mine) came to the rescue. He became a co-partner and the company was re-named the Threlkeld Mining Company. For 25 years the mine was worked with considerable success, yielding a total of 11,000 tons of lead and 14,000 tons of zinc ores, but in 1904 the company went into liquidation.

From 1905 to 1910 the mine was worked by the Threlkeld Syndicate under W. H. Borlase (see Greenside Mine), but problems with water in the low levels forced this company too into liquidation. In 1913 Threlkeld Mines Ltd was formed by Anthony Wilson (see Thornthwaite and Carrock Fell Mine) and was run successfully until 1928.

Blease Gill Trial

On the W bank of Blease Gill, a few yards below the confluence of its two feeders (NY 315267), is a small lead trial level. It is open and starts as a short cross-cut (about 20 ft) before turning W on a badly shattered E-W vein. It follows the vein for about 45 yards. Little mineralisation is present.

Mines of the Glenderaterra Valley

(Brundholme or Glenderaterra Mine, Blencathra Mine)

The northern workings (NY 296273 – NY 296277) constitute Glenderaterra Mine (later called Brundholme Mine) and consist of a number of shafts and levels. The last work was in 1920. The southern working is Blencathra Mine. It consists of a shaft on the E bank of the beck (NY 297267) and a level on the W bank about 200 yards further S. It was last worked c. 1875.

Mining Details

The Blencathra Vein courses approximately N-S and lies on the E side of the beck. The Tebay Lode, on which Brundholme Mine lies, runs along the W side of the stream and where it crosses (NY 296273) splits into two. The western branch has been tried by a level at NY 296277. The main ores were those of lead; smaller amounts of copper ore and baryte were also present. The ore tended to occur in small isolated patches and was in any case of poor quality.

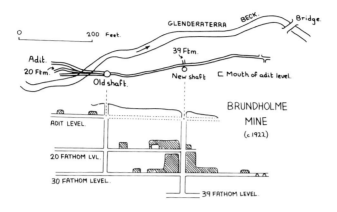

History

(i) Blencathra Mine

This mine is known to have been worked by a number of people in the early 19th century but the first substantial workings were by a Mr J. Crosier who sank a shaft to 25 fathoms (c. 1850). It is not known for how long he stayed but the eventual abandonment was as a result of financial problems not connected with the mine.

In 1866 a Mr Barratt took the mine but gave it up a year later. In 1870 Colonel Watson of Ambleside (who owned the land on the W side of the beck) took a lease on Blencathra Mine, but certainly up to the end of 1871 had no luck at all. It is not known whether he abandoned the mine soon after this, or held it until he abandoned Brundholme Mine in about 1880.

(ii) Brundholme Mine

It is known that John Tebay, who worked a number of the Derwent mines also worked this one, but specific details have not been found. In 1872 Colonel Watson commenced working the mine and took it down to 30 fathoms. The operations were on a very limited scale and abandonment took place some time between 1878 and 1880.

On 21st September 1907, W. H. Borlase (see Greenside and Threlkeld Mines) took over, operating under the name of Brundholme Mining Syndicate Ltd. The existing levels were driven forward and a new shaft sunk but not enough ore was found to make the mine viable. In 1910 all work stopped and by 1915 the company was in liquidation.

W. H. Heywood (see Long Work and Goldscope) took a lease on 8th May

1917 and appointed a Mr Bennett Johns as manager. The levels were extended a little further and the depth increased to 39 fathoms, but once again nothing of real value was found and in June 1920 work seems to have stopped. In 1922 Heywood had the mine evaluated by consulting engineers who declared that the only promising avenue of development would be to try some other lodes in the sett. Thoroughly dispirited, he abandoned the mine.

It has, in several places, been stated that water was often a problem in this mine. This seems reasonable considering the nearby presence of the beck and generally marshy ground. However, several reports state that water was not a problem, the installed pumps coping very well.

Ruthwaite Baryte Mine

The Ruthwaite Baryte Vein follows an almost exact NW-SE course; Gurney's Shaft, the main access, is located at NY 238369, a little N of Ruthwaite. The mine seems to have been first worked in the 1870s, but no records are to be found until for 1910 when it was taken by Messrs Keeble and Jellett. In 1912 Barium Compounds Ltd of Carlisle became the owners and appear to have worked it until 1920.

The vein hades S-W at about 1 fathom in 6 and was generally 12 ft across near outcrop. With increasing depth the baryte became progressively replaced by quartz and rock. By 1920 all baryte had been removed and the mine abandoned.

(see mine section on page 134)

Longlands Copper Mine

A group of copper trials situated on the W flank of Longlands Fell. The Longlands Copper Vein courses 15° W of N and hades to the W. It was reached from three cross-cut adit levels which, from N to S, have the locations NY 272356, NY 271352 and NY 273351 (the middle one now being gated and dammed for use as a water supply). The workings are not extensive and it is unlikely that any of the driving on the vein exceeds 50 fathoms in length.

It was first tried by a Mr Clemence in 1841. He drove two of the levels but finding the vein almost barren soon gave up. In the early 1850s Samuel Merryweather (see Roughtongill) continued the works and drove a new level (probably that at NY 271352). He was a little more successful than Clemence, but not sufficiently so to make the mine pay, and in 1857 the trial was abandoned.

Robin Hood Mine

An antimony mine situated a few yards to the N of Robin Hood House on the E side of the road (NY 227330). It seems to have been active in the 1840s when a shaft was sunk a few fathoms and about 20 tons of antimony ore raised. Subsequently a level was driven with the purpose of unwatering the shaft and locating further deposits, but never completed. The mine was apparently not much of a success and, on closure, the upper part of the shaft was sealed and the level walled up. All the spoil was subsequently used for road surfacing.

The level is now open and runs for a distance of about 150 ft in a NE direction. It shows no sign of mineralisation. About 100 yards to the NE of the level mouth is a small overgrown quarry whose floor contains some vein quartz and small amounts of stibnite and antimony ochres. This might be the site of the old shaft.

High Mill Trial

Situated on the S bank of Chapel Beck, near Bassenthwaite village (NY 239319), this trial consists of a single level which, about 60 ft in, ends in a roof collapse. The only item of information available is a letter dated 1844 stating that a sample of ore obtained from the mine had been analysed and found to contain antimony ore of a superior quality.

Dead Beck Trial

A short level in the ravine of Dead Beck (NY 262312). The trial was for lead, but clearly a failure.

Carl Side Trial

A small trial level on a NW-SE vein at NY 256269. The vein contained mainly baryte, and in the 1870s approximately 150 tons of baryte, containing some good lumps of galena, was supposed to have been removed.

Applethwaite Gill Trial

On the W side of Applethwaite Gill at about the 1,200 ft contour are the scant remains of a shaft, a level and some surface works (NY 270265). The workings are very small and thought to be Elizabethan.

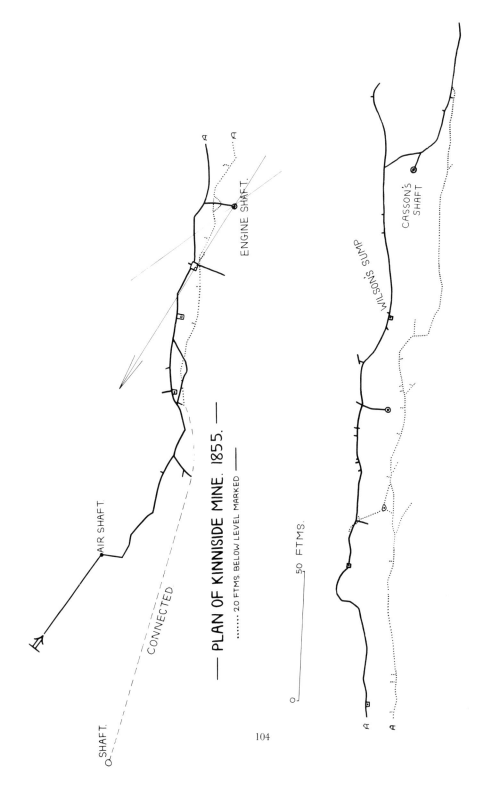

— PLAN OF KINNISIDE MINE. 1855. —

...... 20 FTMS BELOW LEVEL MARKED —

AIR SHAFT

CONNECTED

SHAFT.

ENGINE SHAFT.

50 FTMS.

WILSON'S SUMP

CASSON'S SHAFT

Kinniside Mine

A lead mine situated near Hazleholme which is to the E of Cleator Moor (entrance to top level NY 041148).

Mining Details

The Kinniside Lode runs a course well-approximated by a line drawn from NY 040149 to NY 050141. It hades to the SW at about 1 fathom in 1.5 and yielded galena (8-10 ozs silver per ton of lead metal) and cerussite. It also contained small amounts of copper ore and baryte – even a trifling amount of gold. The ore was worked from two main levels of considerable length and 20 fathoms apart, also from some smaller workings between them. Various other trials have been made in the area but their precise location is uncertain.

Not in the immediate area of Kinniside, but possibly associated with it, is the Black Howe Level at NY 025136. This is of 200 yards total length and contains no significant mineralisation.

History

The earliest date of working is not known, but a report dated 1873 claims it to have been worked 'for at least the last 100 years'.

A lease was taken in 1819 by Messrs Knott and Adam but was subsequently re-assigned, in 1825, to the Egremont and Lonsdale Mining Company which worked the mine for several years before putting it out to tribute. Between 1826 and 1831, 2,200 tons of ore was raised, but in 1833 the depressed state of the lead market forced it to close. All further attempts to work the mine at a profit failed.

In 1853 the Wyndham Consols Mining Company took a lease and in their

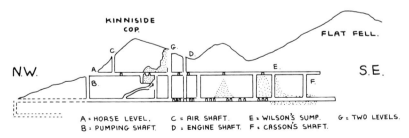

A = HORSE LEVEL.   C = AIR SHAFT.   E = WILSON'S SUMP.   G = TWO LEVELS.
B = PUMPING SHAFT. D = ENGINE SHAFT.   F = CASSON'S SHAFT.

SECTION OF KINNISIDE MINE. A SKETCH MADE FOLLOWING AN EXPLORATION IN 1983. NOT TO SCALE.

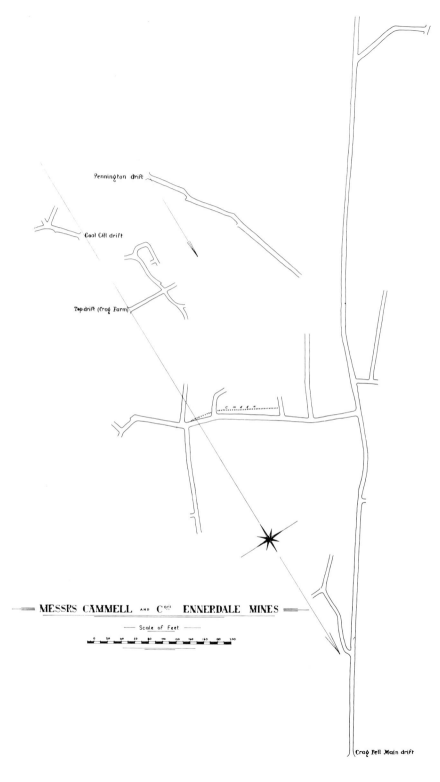

Pennington drift

Coal Gill drift

Top drift (Crag Farm)

C N E E R

MESSRS CAMMELL AND CO. ENNERDALE MINES

Scale of Feet

0 20 40 60 80 100 120 140 160 180 200

Crag Fell Main drift

first year of operation spent £2,000 on developing both the Kinniside Mine and other workings within the sett. By 1856 they had exhausted their capital having spent a total of £2,500, most of it in clearing out collapsed levels and the purchase of tools. Very little ore was raised – 75 tons in 3 years.

Between 1869 and 1873 a Mr Morris Fawcett did some work in the area (probably not on the Kinniside Lode) but by the end of the latter year had lost £3,000. Some trifling exploratory work was done early this century – between the years 1905 and 1912 – but never led to anything successful.

Crag Fell Iron Mines

(Goat Gill Level, Top Drift, Main Drift, Revelin Drift, Pennington Drift, Old Crag Fell Iron Mine, Iron Crag Mine, Various)

The Crag Fell sett consists of numerous small trials and mines on the fells to the S of Ennerdale Water ie Heckbarley, Grike, Crag Fell, The Side and Ennerdale Fell. Most of the workings are very small, though two, Main Drift and Iron Crag Mine, are quite substantial. It is believed that the area has been worked, intermittently, over a period of several hundred years but among all the known workings only one is pre-1860, that being Old Crag Fell Mine (two levels at NY 105139). Any others that once may have existed are now completely lost. Iron Crag Mine (NY 129124) was being worked in 1864 by a lone miner, but no further information in available on the sett until 1873. The records for 1873 and thereafter are not complete but sufficient of them remain to enable the known workings to be dated. The workings, all of them levels, are listed below by grid reference. Accompanying a reference is the level name (if it had one), the date(s) it was worked and the person(s) who worked it. Four lessees are involved and are abbreviated as follows; EdP = Elias de Pass; AB = Alexander Brogden and Sons; RE = Richard Eaton; CC = Charles Cammell and Company.

NY 072147⎤ EdP
NY 077150⎦ 1873
NY 078147 Goal Gill (now called Goat Gill) Level CC 1896.
NY 083149 Red Gill Level AB 1875. CC 1896: under this ownership the level
    was driven forward with the intention of connecting it to Main Drift for
    ventilation.
NY 084150 Main Drift. CC 1895, 1896.
NY 084146 Top Drift. CC 1896.
NY 085146 RE 1881, 1882.
NY 096146 Revelin Drift. CC 1896.
NY 099142 Eaton No 3. RE 1881.
NY 101145 Angler's Crag Level. EdP 1873. AB 1874, 1875.
NY 101142 Eaton No. 2. RE 1881.
NY 103141 Eaton No 1. RE 1881: 50 tons of ore removed. CC 1896: name changed
    to Pennington Drift.

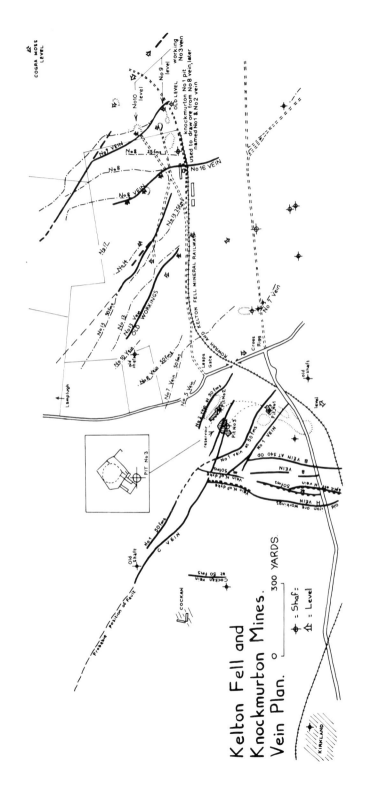

Kelton Fell and
Knockmurton Mines.
Vein Plan.

300 YARDS.

⬦ = Shaft
⬧ = Level

NY 105139 Old Crag Fell Mine. ? 2 levels.
NY 107138 RE 1881.
NY 129124 Iron Crag Mine. ? 1864. RE 1881: 500 tons of ore removed.
NY 134119 RE 1882.
NY 139126 RE 1882.
NY 136135]
NY 145135} Very probably RE 1882.
NY 149135]

The mouths of all these levels are collapsed and some are very difficult to find. All the lessees had great hopes of the sett and could not understand why the successes of nearby iron mines (e.g. Kelton and Knockmurton) were not repeated here. Richard Eaton actually got as far as promoting a Bill in Parliament for the construction of a railway to run from Kelton Fell to Ennerdale for the purpose of transporting huge tonnages which were anticipated but never materialised.

In December 1896 Main Drift was walled up. Nothing has been done on the sett since.

Kelton and Knockmurton Mines

A widespread system of haematite mines situated on the slopes of Knock Murton Fell (NY 095190), Kelton Fell (NY 095180) and Kelton Park (NY 085183).

The workings on Knock Murton, commenced about 1853, were the earlier by a few years than those on Kelton Fell. Unfortunately, many of the reports on these mines have been lost and it is therefore not possible to give a detailed history. A number of plans of some of the larger workings have survived but are rather too complex to reproduce here: instead is included a vein plan. A recent exploration of No 9 level on No 3 vein turned up some very interesting finds and these are shown on another diagram.

Most of the major works are due to William Baird and Company of Rowrah which worked the sett from about 1870 to 1914. The mines were very prosperous over this period, producing from 15,000 to 60,000 tons of haematite per year. A railway, the Rowrah and Kelton Fell line, was constructed to take away their produce but is now dismantled. By 1914 many of the veins had been worked out and the mine was abandoned.

Nothing further happened until about 1920 when the St Nicholas Mining Company of Whitehaven re-opened No 9 and No 10 levels on No 3 vein. In 1923 the Kirland Iron Ore Company Ltd made some explorations near Kirland. Both works were probably abandoned within a year of their commencement.

As this area is not one normally included on fell walks, the intended visitor to the mine should make for the point where the old railway crosses

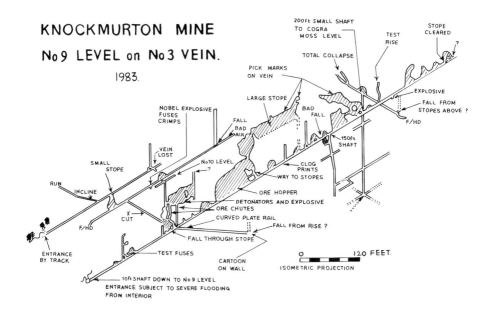

KNOCKMURTON MINE

No 9 LEVEL on No 3 VEIN.

1983.

the Croasdale-Felldyke road. (NY 087183). The landscape here is rather dreary, the purple spoil heaps dotted here and there giving it a slightly odd quality. By following the course of the old railway eastward, a young and particularly impenetrable pine wood is soon reached, which itself hides many major workings. At this point the path splits into two parallel branches. The lower one passes some spoil heaps upon which some nice lumps of haematite can be found, and a few hundred yards on, the lower path rejoins the upper. A short distance further along one is confronted with a totally unexpected – and quite breathtaking – view of the Cogra basin.

Croasdale Iron Mine

Along Hole Gill and also on the banks of Croasdale Beck in the neighbour-hood of the Hole Gill waterfall are a number of iron levels (NY 098180). Until 1873, when the boundary of the Kelton and Knockmurton sett was enlarged to incorporate them, they belonged to the very small Croasdale Iron Ore Royalty. About five levels were involved, three of which are still open. Of the latter, two are more or less opposite each other on the banks of Croasdale Beck at the eastern end of the ravine (NY 099179). These are driven for a short distance only, but the remaining open level at the foot of the Hole Gill waterfall is over 1,200 ft long. All three levels are devoid of significant mineralisation.

The long level at the foot of the waterfall (the Croasdale Level) was started in March 1865 by the Lonsdale Red Haematite Iron Ore Company. Hereafter matters became rather confusing for a lease dated 19th August 1867 is found assigning the Royalty to Messrs Dobson, Wright and Cartwright and yet in 1868 the level is reported as still being driven by the former company. In 1869 financial problems caused work to be suspended and in 1872 the sett was abandoned. In 1873 William Baird and Company commenced extending the level and continued until October 1875 but no worthwhile veins were cut. Shortly afterwards the level was sealed. No work has been done here since.

Loweswater Mines

(Loweswater Mine, Kirkgill Wood Mine)

Loweswater Lead Mine was accessed by two shafts, the NW or Old Wheel Shaft being located at NY 146216 and situated adjacent to Moss Cottage (which was constructed from the old mine building). The last major work here was in about 1841 and both shafts are known to have been almost completely full of rubble by 1856. In 1968 the remaining few feet of the Flat Rod Shaft was filled in, so now there are scant traces of the mine.

In Kirkgill Wood, to the SW of the Loweswater Mine, are two levels very close to the edge of Park Beck; the S level is at NY 140208 and the N at NY 139209. The S level was worked about 1839 and possibly again in 1869, though the latter date is not certain.

On the S side of Scalehill Bridge, just above the car park (NY 149215) is a cutting leading to a level whose entrance is now buried. Nearby is a pit with a drainage ditch. According to local tradition the level was known as Batey's Cave and is supposed to run under the Scale Hill Hotel (highly unlikely!).

To the N of Loweswater Mine a fairly long trial level (open) has been driven into the steep W bank of the River Cocker just below Cold Keld (NY 148221).

Mining Details

The Loweswater vein runs in a NW-SE line from Whinny Ridding to about 50 yards SE of Moss Cottage; it then swings round about 30° or so crossing the River Cocker very close to the N side of Scalehill Bridge.

Prior to about 1840 the mine was worked from 20, 30 and 40 fathom levels as shows on the plan, but soon after a 50 fathom level was driven eastwards from the Flat Rod Shaft. The new level struck a small vein and this produced

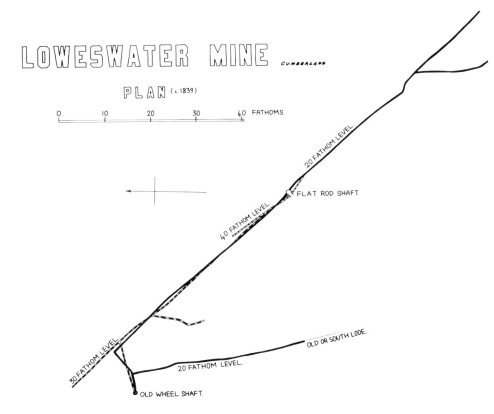

LOWESWATER MINE CUMBERLAND

PLAN (c 1839)

0   10   20   30   40 FATHOMS

20 FATHOM LEVEL

FLAT ROD SHAFT

40 FATHOM LEVEL

30 FATHOM LEVEL

OLD OR SOUTH LODE.

20 FATHOM LEVEL.

OLD WHEEL SHAFT.

many tons of ore, but on sinking to a depth of 70 fathoms the yield dropped off considerably. The richest part of the mine was in the region bounded from below by the 30 fathom level and from the sides by the two shafts. Almost all the vein here was stoped out. Good ore was also found to the E of the Flat Rod Shaft as far down as the 40 fathom level.

The mine was exceedingly wet and had to be drained by pumps driven by a water-wheel supplied via a leat from Crabtree Beck.

According to old geological maps the two Kirkgill Wood levels lie on a NW-SE vein. The S level enters the hill on a course 60° W of S and at about 20 ft in from the entrance there is a small hole beyond which there is a 21 ft deep flooded shaft. Beyond the shaft the level follows the course of the vein and some 30 ft further on from the former terminates in a blockage, the other side of which can be seen from outside, about 50 ft to the right of the present access level. The shaft is referred to in the old records as the Steel Shaft and is reported as being 54 ft deep (probably now partially filled with rubble). It is supposed to have yielded some good lead and copper ore.

The Kirkgill Wood N level is 100 ft long and runs almost due N. It was probably a cross-cut made to locate the NW part of the vein but seems to have failed, there being no traces of mineralisation. Associated with this working is a well concealed 10 ft long level on the opposite side of the beck.

The Scalehill Bridge workings are very small-scale and almost certainly exploited the southern end of the Loweswater vein.

The Cold Keld level is an isolated trial driven on a strong E-W quartz vein.

History

Loweswater Vein was discovered in 1816 during land drainage work, and the mineral rights leased in 1819 by Messrs Joseph Skelton and Skelton Wood. The exact length of their stay is not known but they certainly obtained a large quantity of ore. In 1839 it was leased by Messrs Mellor, Pratchett, Jones, Clemence (elder and younger) and Sealby, with William Jeffrey as manager. This company worked the E end of the mine but failure to find good ore in the 70 fathom level, and the loss of about £6,000, caused abandonment of the venture in about 1841.

The Kirkgill Wood S level was worked in 1839 by Isaac Sealby of the above company, and probably also in the 1860s by Messrs Robinson and Waugh who, holding the lease to an adjoining mining property, are known to have been trying to get their boundary extended to include Kirkgill Wood S level. Nothing is known about the N level, but it was almost certainly driven by one or both of the groups associated with the S one.

Whiteoak Mines
(Whiteoak Mine, Mosedale Mine)

Whiteoak Lead Mine is located at NY 130199, and Mosedale Lead Mine – which could probably be better described as a trial – is located at NY 136186. Whiteoak Mine was last worked in 1891 and this date also sets a upper limit for Mosedale Mine.

Mining Details

Whiteoak Mine exploited a feeble and poorly-mineralised NW-SE vein, the workings consisting of several levels and one shaft. The major working was the lowest level near the side of the beck, now walled up for many years due, apparently, to the nuisance it presented to fox hunters. Near this level are traces of the old buildings, also a pit for a 40 ft water-wheel.

Mosedale Mine lies on three small and very poorly-mineralised veins, one NS, one NW-SE and one SW-NE. It was worked from a few short levels and openworks, but quite clearly was not a success.

History

Whiteoak Mine was leased in 1864 by Messrs Steel, Robinson and Waugh, then held for only one year, 1887, by Henry Vercoe, the holder of many Derwent mines leases.

On 30th April 1888 the Loweswater Lead Company, specifically formed to work the mine, took a lease but the venture rapidly failed. By August 1891 the shareholders refused to supply more money, the chairman had died and the company had been put into liquidation. On 28th July 1892 some of the equipment was put up for sale and the rest transferred to Threlkeld Mine. One of the directors of the Loweswater company was John Sawrey, a founder of the Buttermere Green Slate Company.

Nothing is known about Mosedale Mine other than it was included in the lease of Whiteoak, and thus would have been worked by one or more lessees of the latter.

Floutern Tarn Sett

(Red Gill Level, Gale Fell Levels, Scale Force Level)

This iron ore royalty occupies a broad band of land between Floutern Tarn and Crummock Water. Very little work was done here and one has to look hard to find any evidence. Nevertheless, should anyone wish to try, the grid references of some known sites are Red Gill level, NY 128170; Gale Fell levels (two in the neighbourhood of NY 139167 and one at NY 140167); and Scale Force level near the foot of the waterfall, NY 151171. There are two other levels somewhere on the rough N face of Gale Fell but insufficient information precludes giving their precise locations. All were very small, never developing into true mines, and nothing has been done hereabouts since 1873, possibly a little earlier.

Mining Details

The only available information on these trials comes from a report dated 1873, but alas one so vague as not to give the precise location of the veins, nor the dates on which work was done. It would seem that nine veins were known, one at the Red Gill level (an E-W vein), one at the Scale Force level (a N-S lode) and seven N-S lodes very closely bunched together on Gale Fell. The report states the Red Gill level to be collapsed, the Scale Force level open and 18 fathoms long, and the other levels to be between 8 and 45 fathoms long. Clearly the total tonnages of ore obtained must have been very small.

History

The earliest known occupant of this sett was the Loweswater Iron and Lead Ore Company in 1863, but to what extent they were responsible for the above works is not known.

In the late 1860s a Mr Faithful Cookson and a mining engineer, John Hosking, were searching the whole of West Cumberland for available iron ore properties, subsequently taking leases at Eskdale, Knockmurton and Floutern Tarn. Either Cookson was extraordinarily lucky or a very shrewd businessman for, in 1871, after the Franco-Prussian War there was a tremendous boom in the iron trade and for a time the price of iron ore skyrocketed. It was merely a matter of waiting and soon a buyer was knocking at the door in the shape of the Whitehaven Iron Mines Ltd, a company specifically formed in 1871 to work the Eskdale, Knockmurton and Floutern Royalties. For a while Cookson sub-let the mines – at a price no doubt – and later sold the leases.

The Whitehaven company had simply taken on too much and despite having £95,000 of capital was still not in a position to develop three sites at once, therefore Knockmurton was given up very quickly. Although the company held on to Floutern until 1877 it was never able to allocate sufficient resources to do any work on it; Eskdale, alas, had taken up all available money. Various estimates prepared for the company relating to work needed at Floutern – the building of accommodation, provision of roads, railways and the like – showed there to be hugely differing sums required. Thus £20,000 would, so to speak, buy a budget job, but a proper one could cost as much as £120,000.

Melbreak Trials

There are two iron trials, one on the W side and one of the E side of Melbreak (NY 142192, NY 148196). Both go into the mountain for only a few feet and lie on the same SW-NE vein.

Buttermere Mine

A copper mine very close to the western shore of Buttermere (NY 180157). It was worked by the Elizabethans in 1569/70, and by Messrs Knott and Taylor from 1822 to 1825. The lakeside path passes over the spoil heap.

Honister Try Level

A 50 ft long copper trial which passes under the Honister Pass road (NY 223137). It follows a strong NE quartz vein containing spots of malachite and a steel-grey micaceous haematite. The vein has also been tried where it re-appears half way up the spoil heaps of Rigghead Quarries. This level, hard to find, is about 60 ft long.

Low Wax Knott Trial

To locate, follow the path up to Scarth Gap until it passes over the top of a small crag. Below this is a level and openworks (NY 188141). It is known to have been worked towards the end of the 19th century by two men living a rough existence in a small hut nearby, and who, when the weather was reasonable, went down each night to the village local. Eventually they stopped appearing and a search located the body of one of them in a deep pool at Warnscale bottom. It was suspected one had murdered the other and taken off.

Liza Beck Trial

There is a small working on the E side of the beck (NY 157222) where some galena was found.

Gasgale Gill Trial

This is on the N side of Gasgale Gill (NY 164210) and to reach it necessitates a short scramble up a rough slope. It is a hole 10 ft long containing no mineralisation, and perhaps was the beginning of an attempt to locate the Force Crag Vein on whose course it lies.

Rannerdale Trial

Just before rounding Hause Point on the way to Buttermere a 5 ft square hole can be seen up in the crags (NY 163183). It goes in about 6 ft and at its end there are two small quartz strings containing a little galena.

Beckside Trial

At the edge of Buttermere is a small car-parking area, the flattened spoil heap of two small lead workings on the other side of the road (NY 192154). The low level is 30 ft long and the upper 15 ft, and both are well concealed.

Blackbeck Trial

By following the stream down from Blackbeck Tarn some vein material containing traces of galena may be found. A very small working can be seen where the ravine opens out a little further down (NY 201131).

Sosgill Trial

Near Bramley Farm is a 10 ft long trial level (NY 103237). Hereabouts must be considerable lead contamination, for in 1968 the farmer is recorded as saying he was unable to keep ducks, lead poisoning eventually killing them.

Iron Mines of Eskdale

(Nab Gill Mine, Blea Tarn Mine, Mecklin Park Mine, Mines North of Christcliff, Brant Rake Mine, Gill Force and Gate Crag Mines, Ban Garth Mine)

There are a number of haematite mines on the N and S sides of the Eskdale Valley, these being:

Nab Gill Mine – NY 175012
Blea Tarn Mine – NY 167007
Mecklin Park Mine – NY 129020
Several small mines north of Christcliff – NY 185011
Brant Rake Mine – SD 149985
Gill Force and Gate Crag Mines – SD 180999
Ban Garth Mine – NY 153008

The largest is Nab Gill Mine, the levels of which were driven from the ravine of Nab Gill above Boot. All were abandoned by the mid-1880s except

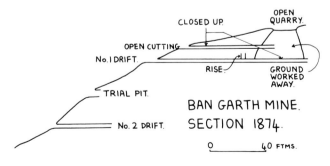

for Nab Gill, re-opened for a short time in 1909 and again in 1917. None of these mines was a commercial success, but without them there would never have existed the delightful Ravenglass & Eskdale Railway, originally constructed for the conveying of iron ore.

Mining Details

The Nab Gill vein hades E and courses 35° W of N. The OS map shows a drift at NY 163027 which, lying on the vein's course, was probably an attempt to test its northern continuation. The vein was rich at outcrop but

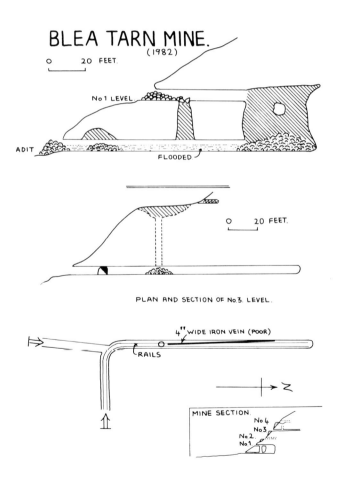

BLEA TARN MINE.
(1982)

No 1 LEVEL

ADIT

FLOODED

PLAN AND SECTION OF No3. LEVEL.

4" WIDE IRON VEIN (POOR)

RAILS

MINE SECTION.
No 4
No 3
No 2
No 1

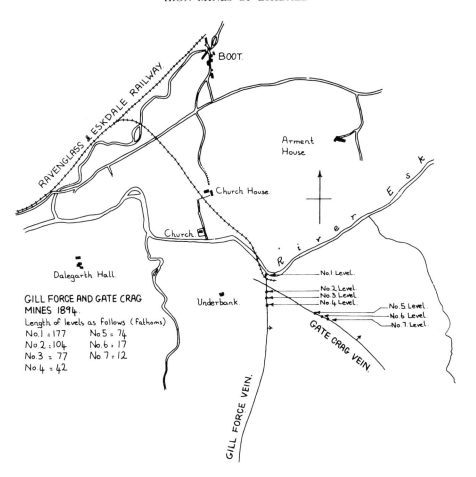

GILL FORCE AND GATE CRAG
MINES 1894.
Length of levels as follows (fathoms)

No.1 = 177	No.5 = 74
No.2 = 104	No.6 = 17
No.3 = 77	No.7 = 12
No.4 = 42	

at depth narrowed and became very poor. Its western branch, the Mitredale Side Vein, was tried but found unpromising.

To the W of Nab Gill, just above Beckfoot Station, is the Blea Tarn Mine, lying on an approximately N-S vein called the Blea Tarn Lode. The vein was poor and yielded only one good pocket of ore.

Mecklin Park Mine lies on three adjacent N-S veins and its first two years of operation yielded 1,200 tons of ore. An old report claims the veins to be of high quality, but as it was couched to attract potential purchasers of the mine, it shouldn't be taken too seriously.

The mines N of Christcliff are all fairly small and it is unlikely that much ore was found.

Brant Rake Mine lies on a N-S vein and, though reported to have yielded

SSE.

No.1 LEVEL.

No. 2 LEVEL.

No. 3 LEVEL.

No. 4 LEVEL.

No. 5 LEVEL.

A

A

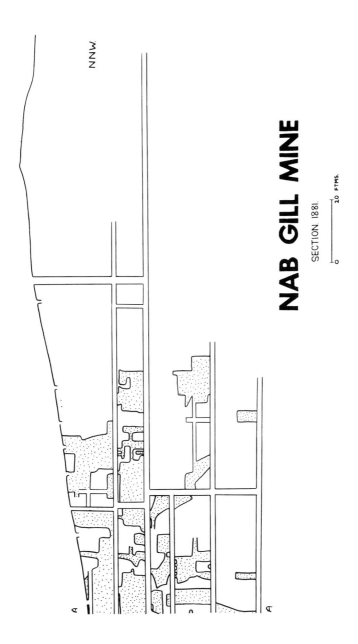

NAB GILL MINE

SECTION 1881.

NNW.

0   20 FTMS.

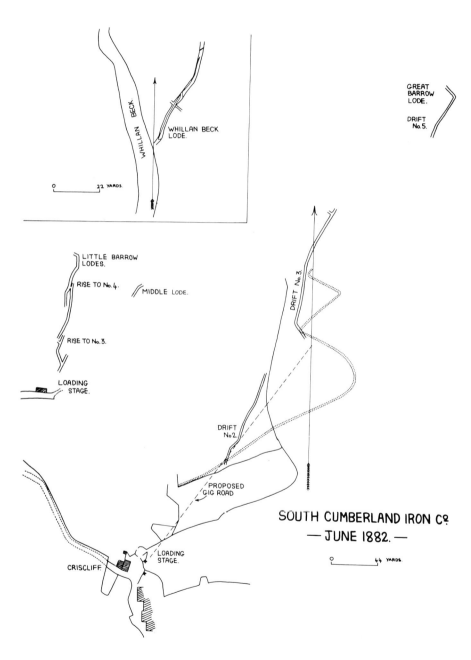

good ore, was never properly opened out. The workings consist of three levels and some surface works.

The Gill Force and Gate Crag veins intersect at a point a little to the E of Underbank. In the neighbourhood of this junction, seven levels were driven with an aggregate length of 503 fathoms, and a total of 5,300 tons of ore obtained over a period of about four years.

Ban Garth Mine lies on an approximately N-S vein and contained a small amount of ore much intermingled with crushed rock.

History

In September 1845, Messrs S. & J. Lindow took a lease on the area covering Ban Garth and Nab Gill Mines, and spent considerable money driving levels at Nab Gill, but by 1854 seem to have lost interest, transferring their men to Ban Garth. Unfortunately, this also turned out to be a disappointment and around 1856 the pair withdrew from the venture. In 1860 a Mr. Joseph Fearon took on Ban Garth but, being no luckier than his predecessors, gave up in the late 1860s.

At about this time, the area between and including Nab Gill and Ban Garth was leased by Faithful Cookson. Mr Cookson and his probable motivation for leasing iron ore properties are dealt with elsewhere under the heading of the Floutern Tarn Sett, and apply here. In 1871 he sub-let to the Whitehaven Iron Mines Ltd, a company specifically formed to work Eskdale, Floutern Tarn and part of Knockmurton but which in practice worked only Eskdale.

This company drove a new level below the old Ban Garth workings and started Blea Tarn Mine, but soon all its efforts were put into Nab Gill. The ore yield was not particularly good, but the main problem arose through the high cost of carting ore to Ravenglass by road. Thus 1872 saw the promotion of a Bill in Parliament seeking permission to construct a railway. On 26th May 1873 'The Ravenglass and Eskdale Railway Act' was passed, and the line opened for public goods traffic on 24th May 1875. Its cost of £32,000 was borne by the Whitehaven company and the contractor, Mr Oliver, each contributing £12,000, the residue being raised by an issue of debenture bonds.

Despite the railway, however, the company's fortune continued to decline and by 1881 the selling price of ore (30 shillings per ton in 1871; 8 shillings per ton in 1881) had sunk so low that it was forced into liquidation. The total ore raised by this company was about 50,000 tons and, for a short while afterwards, sporadic but unsuccessful attempts were made by others to re-start the mine.

In 1909 Messrs J. B. Swann, W. B. Hardie and J. Laird re-opened the bottom level of Nab Gill and, sinking below it, obtained an amount of ore too small to make the venture viable. In 1912 they abandoned it. The last attempt was in 1917, when four men worked the bottom level for a period of a year or so. The tonnages obtained, however, were very small.

The mines N of Christcliff and those on the Gate Crag and Gill Force veins were commenced (or re-opened) by Messrs Donaldson and Allport in 1880 and worked until 1884. It is interesting to note that a branch line from the Eskdale Railway to their southern workings was constructed without Parliamentary permission.

Mecklin Park Mine was started in 1872 and in 1874 was in the hands of Messrs Saunders and Scott who sub-leased it from Lindow. They seemed anxious to sell the mine but whether they did so is not known.

Brankenwalls Gill Iron Mine

A group of workings above Muncaster Mill. There are three levels in the neighbourhood of SD 102977, two of which are open. The lowest level is clear for 350 ft and the middle one for about 150 ft. In the wood below are another two levels. By the side of the tarn is a short trial level and a surface working (SD 105977).

Taw House Copper Trials

In June 1857 a Whitehaven group, Messrs Barnes and Company, commenced copper trials near Taw House. There are two levels: one at NY 207013 and 150 ft long, the other at NY 205013 and 30 ft long.

Spot How Gill Copper Mine

Situated at NY 205004, this consists of two distinct workings. The lower is a level with an air shaft; the higher is a level with two branches. The entrance to the E branch is by the side of the gill. A few yards to the S, in higher ground, is a short level containing a 20 ft deep shaft. The foot of this shaft connects to the W branch.

Buckbarrow Beck Mine

A small copper mine consisting of a 130 yard long level and a surface trial (SD 136908). There are no stopes in the level and the quality of the material on the dumps is poor.

Holehouse Gill or Hesk Fell Mine

A fairly large copper mine consisting of three levels (SD 175942). The lowest is 91 yards long but no information is available on the other two. The middle working is by far the largest and a cluster of ruined mine buildings are to be seen at the top of its substantial spoil heap. There is a good deal of chalcopyrite and arsenopyrite in the dumps of the middle and top level.

Logan Beck Mine

A fairly large copper mine on the W bank of Logan Beck (SD 173916). The most southerly working is a level (length unknown) with a small flattened dump. A few yards to the N is a large spoil heap. At the top of this heap is the collar of a 53 ft deep flooded shaft. At the foot of the heap is a ruined building. On the immediate S side of this building is the entrance to a 165 yard long level. This level has several flooded pits in its floor which probably connect with deeper workings.

Bowscale Beck Mine

A small copper mine situated on the banks of Bowscale Beck (SD 172909). On the S bank is a small spoil heap and a few yards to the W there is a level driven into the N bank. The level goes in for only 12 yards or so before terminating in a roof collapse. There is a dangerous false floor and an 18 ft deep flooded sump a few feet in from the entrance.

Ulpha Copper Mine

There are several levels in Stonegarth Wood (SD 186924) and near to the S side of the road is a shaft. The shaft is about 40 ft deep and at its foot is a level, 370 yards of which is driven in a westerly direction. The eastern extent of the level is not known for sure (blocked with rubbish) but it almost certainly crosses under the road and emerges somewhere in the wood (entrance lost).

The mine is known to have been worked in the 1860s, and in 1874 some prospecting was done by Messrs Burnyeat Brown and Company. From 1880 to 1884 a Samuel Sherwen directed operations and in 1888 Messrs Walker and Peile took the lease. The latter party cleaned out the levels and were ready to start production when a dispute over mineral rights brought work to a halt. Whether they continued after matters were resolved is not known.

Black Beck Mine

A group of copper workings in the neighbourhood of SD 173888. There are several short levels, some surface works and the remains of a shaft.

Whitecombe Beck Mine

There are a number of levels and surface works on the E and W banks of Whitecombe Beck, lying between SD 150850 and SD 150860. The major working appears to be the level at SD 152857: this is 300 ft long but contains no stopes or other features of interest. The mine was for copper and exploited a NE-SW system of veins.

High Brow Sulphur Mine

An iron pyrite mine some two miles to the N of Millom (SD 182835). The mine's name and the yellow material that coats the rocks of its interior can give the impression that native sulphur was found here but this is not so. The yellow material appears to be a mineral of the jarosite group and the term sulphur used often to be applied to iron pyrite, at one time a major source of sulphur.

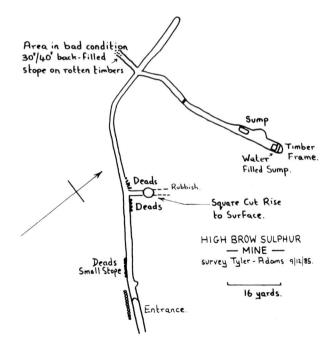

Area in bad condition 30'/40' back-filled Stope on rotten timbers

Sump

Timber Frame.
Water Filled Sump.

Deads
Rubbish.
Square Cut Rise to Surface.
Deads

HIGH BROW SULPHUR
— MINE —
survey Tyler - Adams 9/12/85.

16 yards.

Deads
Small Stope

Entrance.

The mine was started in 1851 by persons unknown and the iron pyrite sent to Newcastle for processing. For how long the mine ran under this tenancy is not known, but in September 1865 the operators became Messrs Walton and Cowper (see Force Crag and Threlkeld mines). As with the previous ownership there is no record of the duration of their stay or of the success of the venture.

Whicham Trial

On the hillside above Whicham, and quite obvious from the road, is a 15 ft long level (SD 130829). Nearby are a number of overgrown pits and scratchings on the N-S system of quartz strings. The mineral sought was probably copper pyrite.

Raven Crag Trial

Just below Raven Crag near Swinside Farm is a fairly large spoil heap (SD 168883). The level mouth is closed but the quantity of spoil suggests a drive of 100-200 yards. The trial was probably for copper ore.

Middle Kinmont Mine

A small haematite mine situated on the embankment to the E of, and opposite, the derelict buildings of Middle Kinmont Farm (SD 118905). There are two distinct sites within the sett. One is located where a small brook crosses the path to Low Kinmont Farm and consists of a single shaft. The other is about 100 yards to the N where an E-W stone wall meets the main N-S stream. This consists of two flooded shafts and a rather odd rake-shaped earthwork which may be associated with one or more old levels. Both workings are very overgrown. The mine was worked by persons unknown at various intervals between 1835 and 1860.

Greenside Mine

Situated at the W end of Glenridding Screes (NY 365174), Greenside Lead Mine is the greatest success story of Lake District mining. It operated almost continuously for 200 years, yielding a total of some 2,400,000 tons of ore and 2,000,000 ozs of silver, all from a single vein. By 1962 all economically recoverable ore had been removed and the mine was was abandoned.

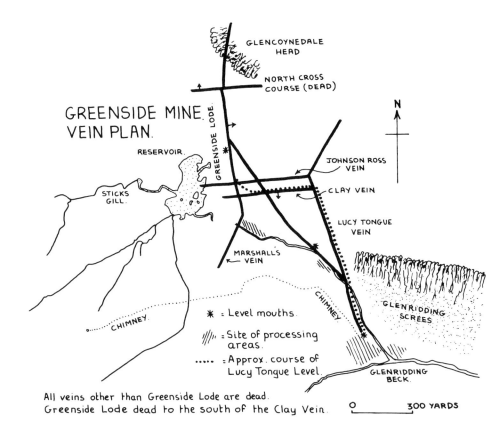

GREENSIDE MINE.
VEIN PLAN.

All veins other than Greenside Lode are dead.
Greenside Lode dead to the south of the Clay Vein.

Mining Details

The Greenside Lead Vein hades E at about 1 fathom in 3 and has a N-S course. Intersecting it are a number of other veins, all devoid of worthwhile ore. The vein filling was argentiferous galena (about 10 ozs silver per ton of lead metal) in a matrix of quartz and smashed country-rock. A fair amount of baryte was also found in the higher workings but at a time when of no commercial value. The vein was sometimes very wide in the high workings – 60 ft or more – but in the deeper ones its width stayed close to an average value of about 8 ft. Small amounts of blende and a trifling amount of copper pyrite were found in the vein too, especially in the deeper levels, but never in workable quantities.

The earliest workings were from levels high up on the fellside but as the mine got deeper, lower and longer levels were progressively driven, the lowest being Lucy Tongue Level, started in 1853 and completed in 1869.

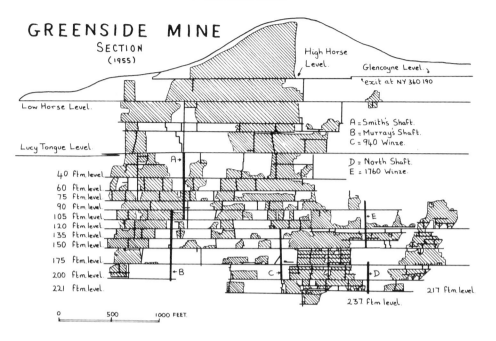

When the mine closed its deepest workings were 1,420 ft below Lucy Tongue Level and 3,000 ft below the top of the hill.

History

The earliest evidence of mining at what was probably Greenside Mine is to be found in James Clarke's *A Survey of the Lakes*, which first appeared in 1787. This dates the earliest operations *c.* 1750. Clarke's article is interesting and worth quoting:

> Patterdale, though now the poorest place that I am acquainted with, was once the seat of peace and plenty. Almost every man had a small freehold, whose annual produce (though perhaps not equal to the daily expenditure of the rich and gay), not only maintained him and his family in a comfortable manner, but even enabled many among them to amass small sums of money. The scene is now changed; Vice and poverty sit pictured in almost every countenance, and the rustic fireplace is no longer the abode of peace and contentment. This lamentable change took place about thirty years ago; at this time some lead mines were wrought in the Dale, and of course a number of miners brought from different parts for the purpose. These fellows who are in general the most abandoned, wicked and profligate part of mankind, no sooner settled here, then they immedi-

ately began to propagate their vices among the innocent unsuspecting inhabitants. The farmer listened greedily to stories of places he had never seen, and by that means was brought to drink and at length to game with these miscreants: his daughters, allured by promises, were seduced; even those who withstood promises and were actually married, were, upon the stopping of the mines, deserted by their faithless husbands, and left to all the horrors of poverty and shame.

Nothing more is known until sometime between 1810 and 1820 when a group of four gentlemen met in the Angel Inn, Penrith, to discuss the prospects of opening out the lead mines at Patterdale, abandoned some years previously. Under the leadership of Thomas Cant, a Penrith grocer, this group financed lead mining for a number of years, and in 1822 formed the Greenside Mining Company. Initially, profits were fairly small, but by 1840 the company was highly prosperous, so much so that in 1827 a 1/64th share was worth £100; in 1837 the same share was worth £1,000!

By 1853 the workings had gone below the Low Level and a mining engineer, J. C. Cain, was called in to survey the mine and advise on the positioning of a new low level. On 6th May 1853, Cain presented his report which offered the company two alternatives for the new level. The first was a direct 556 fathom drive through hard rock; this to take $23\frac{1}{2}$ years to complete with 24 hours a day working. The second was a 693 fathoms drive through the softer ground of the Lucy Tongue and Clay Veins; this to take $19\frac{1}{2}$ years of round the clock driving, and for which the company opted. Later that year work commenced, and the Lucy Tongue Level was completed in 1869 after 16 years' driving under the most unpleasant of working conditions.

In 1891 under W. H. Borlase, the manager, Smith's Shaft was sunk and the mine made history by being the first in Britain to install electric winding gear at the shaft top. The electricity was generated by means of water from Kepple Cove Tarn driving turbines coupled to 600 volt dynamos. So successful was the use of electric power that generating capacity was progressively increased, the water for the turbines coming from Red Tarn at the foot of Helvellyn; Brown Cove at the foot of Catstye Cam; Top Dam, an artificial lake that has all but disappeared, by the side of the path over Sticks Pass; and, of course, Kepple Cove. In 1893 the mine achieved another first by installing an electric locomotive to run along Lucy Tongue Level, transporting ore to the mill.

To regress for a moment, in the very early days of the mine the ore was transported over the mountain and along the Vale of St John to Keswick, thence to a smelter at Stoneycroft Gill, but in 1820, and for the next ten years or so, it was sent to Alston. In the 1830s smelting and desilvering works were built at the mine and from the furnaces an arched chimney of stone ran for about a mile up the fellside, creating not only a draught but also serving to catch the valuable lead dust in the smoke. Every so often some poor souls had the job of sweeping it out and returning the dust to the furnaces. In the early years of the 20th century the Greenside smelter closed, and the dressed ore was sent to more modern and efficient smelters at Newcastle.

Though production was greatly reduced during the First World War, the Greenside Company continued in business until 1935, when a serious fall in the price of lead forced it into liquidation. The company's financial problems had also been exacerbated by the Kepple Cove Dam burst during the very stormy night of Saturday, 29th October 1927, when, at 1.45 a.m. the earth dam was breached leaving a gap 80 ft wide by 60 ft deep. This produced a huge wave which roared down the valley doing considerable damage on the way. In Glenridding many windows were smashed, buildings flooded and much structural damage was sustained. The compensation paid by the company was heavy.

In 1936 the Basinghall Mining Syndicate Limited took over and for a number of years the mine, once again, flourished. However, it soon became clear that the Greenside Vein could not last much longer, and, in 1947, a vigorous programme of underground and surface exploration was initiated in the hope of finding new deposits. Nothing was found.

Despite many vicissitudes the mine's story would have been fairly uneventful were it not for two tragic accidents, the first of which occurred on 7th July 1952. During the weekend a fire had started in the North Shaft and carbon monoxide found its way into various parts of the workings. When a group of miners approached the 940 winze early on Monday morning they were driven back by strong fumes, but not before hearing the shouts of miner Leo Mulryan who had descended to the bottom of the winze. In the subsequent attempt to rescue him three men died as did Mulryan himself. The rescue attempt was heroic: several men justly received medals and commendations for their trojan efforts.

The second accident happened in 1960. At this time the mine was about to close but the Atomic Energy Authority obtained permission to carry out underground seismic tests. The intention was to set off some underground charges and to monitor the shock waves, in the hope that the data obtained would serve in determining the magnitude and position of Russian underground nuclear bomb tests. An egg-shaped chamber was excavated and two charges deposited, one of 500 lbs of T.N.T., the other 250 lbs. These were fired electrically from the surface but only the larger one went off. Though the mine was ventilated and eventually declared safe, two men who later went in were poisoned by an isolated pocket of gas in one of the stopes.

The last ore was removed from the mine in April 1961, and in 1962 it was abandoned. Many of the scars left by the mine had been removed prior to its closure; indeed as early as 1940 abortive attempts were made to encourage the growth of vegetation on the vast spoil heaps. However, success was not achieved until the mid-1950s when sewage was sprayed, enabling the plant roots to take hold.

Mines of Grisedale

(Eagle Crag Mine, Ruthwaite Lodge Mine, Hagg Mine)

The three lead mines of Grisedale are Ruthwaite Lodge (NY 355136), Eagle Crag (NY 358142) and Hagg (NY 390158). The first two are of ancient origin and were probably always worked as a single unit finally to be abandoned no later than 1880. Hagg Mine was a short-lived venture and was not worked after 1808. The workings of Ruthwaite Lodge and the considerably larger Eagle Crag Mine are still very evident whereas nothing at all remains of Hagg Mine, the only proof that it ever existed being from a few old documents.

Mining Details

The Ruthwaite Lodge Vein follows a course 70° E of N and can be traced from the shallow workings near the climbing hut to a collapsed level at NY 360138. The spoil from the latter shows very little mineralisation but there is a reasonable presence of galena in the spoil from the former. The workings near the hut are mostly small scale and consist of openworks and two short levels, one of which is rubbish-filled; it is also apparent that some work has been done in the ravine through which the stream flows. The only substantial working is a level that has been driven from the side of the waterfall. This is open and about 450 ft long but except for a little malachite a few yards in from the entrance is devoid of mineralisation.

The Eagle Crag Vein follows an E-W course and has been worked or tried on both sides of the valley. Following its course from E to W the first working encountered is a stone-arched level at NY 365143. The level is open at the mouth but about 15 ft in is collapsed. A fair amount of spoil has come from this level, suggesting a drive of 100 yards or more, but little mineralisation is to be seen so clearly the trial was not a success. The major workings lie close together on Eagle Crag and the spoil from levels Nos 1 to 5 can be seen from the valley floor. No 1 level is about 60 ft above Grisedale Beck: it is about 30 yards long, devoid of mineralisation, and contains no features of interest. No 2 level is open, about 235 yards long, and at 175 yards in there is a narrow rise up to No 3 level. The level has been stoped almost to surface near the entrance but after about 10 yards in, save for a little copper staining in the roof, appears to be barren. Nos 3, 4 and 5 levels are collapsed at their mouths but the large amount of spoil suggests each to have been several hundred yards in length. Between levels 1 to 5 the back of the vein has been worked extensively from pits and trenches. Over the top of the crag are levels Nos 6, 7, 8 and 9. The first two are short and contain deep flooded sumps; the others are closed. Between levels 7 and 8, adjacent to a ruined hut, is a 60 ft deep openwork. The most westerly working is a trial level (closed) with a grassed-over spoil heap at NY 353142.

The Eagle Crag Vein has a branch called the Clay Vein which runs a

NE-SW course from near No 8 level to a level 50 yards N of Nethermostcove Beck. This latter level is open and about 300 yards long, starting as a short drive to the Clay Vein, then turning SW along the vein and following it under the beck.

Hagg Mine consisted of a number of pits, trenches, levels and a shaft, all of which were small. Nothing is known about the vein other than that it was galena-bearing and passed under Home Farm.

History

Both Ruthwaite Lodge and Eagle Crag mines contain examples of hand working of the Elizabethan type which implies them to be at least 16th century. On the 24th May 1784 a lease was taken by Messrs John Walker and John Edmundson, known to have still been working the mines in 1807. That they worked the sett for at least 23 years suggests the venture was a success. The next known occupants were Jacob Johnston and John Pattinson who took a lease on the 7th January 1862: nothing is known of their activities. The last tenant was the Greenside Company who ran the mine from 1872 to no later than 1880.

Hagg Mine was started as a result of galena being found in 1799 during land drainage work. The operator was a Mr Mounsey, the surface tenant. Mounsey doesn't appear to have done very much and in 1806 the mine was taken by John Little and John Monkhouse. Initially Mounsey, still the surface tenant, encouraged the newcomers but later came into conflict with them, alleging their damage and trespass. The row resulted, in 1807, in a court case which seems to have been settled to the satisfaction of all parties. Mining continued until the end of 1808.

Low Hartsop or Myers Head Mine

There are two large workings at this lead mine; a shaft situated at the confluence of Pasture Beck and Hayeswater Gill (NY 416126), and three levels and a shaft cut into the ridge leading up to Hartsop Dodd (NY 410125). The other smaller workings are two levels at NY 417125 (collapsed near their entrances), a level at NY 412129 (closed), and a 60 yard long level at NY 415128. The only records referring start in 1867 and run up to 1875, but the mine was certainly run for a year or two after this date. 1878 would be a fair estimate for the year of final abandonment.

Mining Details

The vein associated with the shaft near the stream follows a NNW-SSE

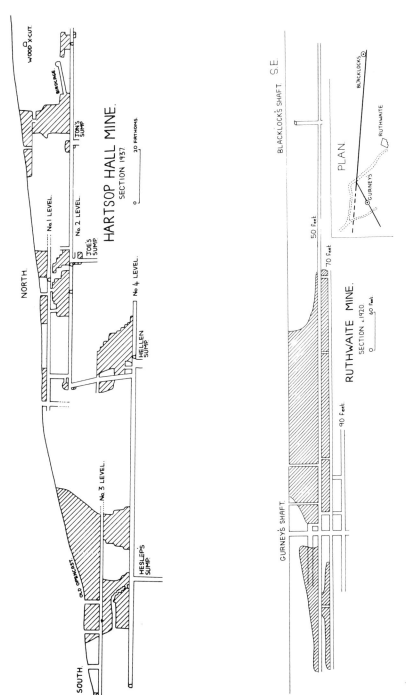

WOOD X-CUT.

BIRDCAGE

NORTH.

TON'S SUMP

No 1 LEVEL.

No 2 LEVEL.

JOE'S SUMP

HARTSOP HALL MINE.

SECTION 1937

No 4 LEVEL.

0   20 FATHOMS

HELLEN SUMP

No 3 LEVEL.

OLD OPENCAST.

HESLEP'S SUMP

SOUTH.

BLACKLOCK'S SHAFT   S.E.

BLACKLOCKS

RUTHWAITE

PLAN

GURNEYS

50 Feet

70 Feet

90 Feet

RUTHWAITE MINE.

SECTION c.1920.

0   60 Feet

GURNEY'S SHAFT.

134

(see text on page 102)

course and contained argentiferous galena (16 ozs of silver per ton of lead metal), blende and a little copper pyrite in a matrix of sandy quartz and crushed rock. The shaft was 30 fathoms deep and from its foot a 12 fathom long cross-cut was driven E on a caunter vein. Where the cross-cut intersected the main vein a level was driven N and S along the side of the latter. No details are available on the N level other than that it was short, very wet, and had to be closed to stop the heavy influx of water. The S level was driven a distance of 150 fathoms, and along the first 94½ fathoms good ore was found when short cross-cuts were driven into the vein; so too was a good deal of sandy water and the cross-cuts had to be closed soon after they were driven. Over the remaining distance the vein passed through a band of slate and the ore values dropped dramatically. The wet crumbly vein was not the only source of trouble, for the ground either side of it was also bad and collapses were frequent.

The vein close to the Hartsop Dodd ridge contained much quartz and a little galena. The lowest level of the three is about 130 fathoms in length, and the one above it 40 fathoms, the two being connected internally by a 200 ft deep shaft. The latter level is connected to surface by a 25 ft deep shaft and above this is a small trial level.

History

Early in 1867 the Low Hartsop Mining Company, run by a Mr Coultas Dodsworth of Haydon Bridge and Messrs Head and Jameson, directors of the Greenside Company, started to sink the shaft near the stream, completing it and reaching the vein in 1868. To unwater it a 30 ft water-wheel was erected and the ruins of the watercourse supports and wheel pit can still be seen. By 1869 the company was experiencing increasingly severe problems with large volumes of sandy water which often blocked, and sometimes overwhelmed, the pumps. From 1870 onwards the shaft was worked only occasionally and most of the work was done elsewhere – probably at the Dodd. Little ore was ever raised and the mine was a commercial failure.

Hartsop Hall Mine

A lead mine situated in the woods above Hartsop Hall (NY 395120). The mine is very old, certainly 17th century and possibly earlier, and has been worked only infrequently. It was abandoned in 1942.

Mining Details

The Hartsop Hall Vein runs NE-SW and hades to the W at about 1 fathom in 3. It was generally about 3 ft wide and contained argentiferous galena (35 ozs silver per ton of lead metal) in a matrix of quartz and smashed country-rock with a good deal of baryte. In depth, small amounts of blende and copper ore were found but nothing worth working. From the plan it will be seen that the ore distribution was patchy.

About half a mile SW of the mine, near Hogget Gill, are the remains of a very old smelter.

History

The earliest lease to have been found is one dated 17th April 1696 which gave mining rights for a 21 year period to Sir Nathaniel Johnson, Alderman of Newcastle-Upon-Tyne, and Robert Jopling, Town and Country Gentleman. No other information concerning this occupancy is known.

The next record is for 1802 when Thomas Dodd, resplendent under the title of 'The Governor and Company for Smelting Down with Pit Coal and Sea Coal of St Martin's Lane, London',* took a lease. He was evidently disappointed for on 4th June 1804 all work was stopped and the mine abandoned.

A document dated March 1867 gives the owners as Messrs Kennedy, Whiteside, Head, Jameson and Coy,† and indicates that they had been working the mine since at least November 1866. By November 1867 the low adit (No 4) had been driven forward 40 fathoms, but in other respects all was not well. The miners were complaining of bad wages and the sloppy manner in which the mine was being run. In addition, operations were severly hindered by a lack of water for driving the crushing and dressing machinery. The company considered erecting a steam engine to provide the necessary power but were deterred from doing so by the high cost of coal. The greater part of 1868 seems to have passed by uneventfully and the few surviving accounts show a monthly production of about 20 tons of ore, but in November the company came into dispute with the surface agricultural tenant, a Mr Backhouse. He claimed that fine particulate matter, a product of dressing operations, was being dumped into the mine stream which passed through his property and was killing fish and injuring livestock. The dispute grew streadily more bitter and the ever present threat of a court order closing the mine discouraged the company from investing in a deeper adit and other

---

* The 'Governor and Company for Smelting Down Lead with Pittcoale and Seacoale' was incorporated by charter on 4th October 1692, and came into being as a result of major advances in smelting technique. The new technology triggered a revival of mining within the country and the work of David Davies, and others, within the Lake District was probably just one manifestation of this. In 1704 a number of Quakers joined the Governor and Company eventually gaining control of it. The Governor and Company, also known as the London Lead Company or the Quaker Lead Company, was responsible for the massive lead mining works in the North Pennines.

† George Head Head and John Jameson were directors of the Greenside Company.

items of expenditure which it felt were needed. Mining continued in a half-hearted fashion but by November 1870 the dispute had worsened to such a degree that all work ceased. In November 1871 the mine was abandoned.

In 1931, it was re-opened by a syndicate consisting of W. T. Shaw, T. Shaw and J. Myles, but shortly afterwards the low price of lead forced the mine's closure. The same body re-opened it in 1934 but lack of capital precluded work of any consequence. However, in April 1941, J. H. Clay of Caldbeck Mines Ltd joined the syndicate and Hartsop Mines Limited was formed. Work continued for a short while, with rather more vigour, but wartime conditions created problems and the mine was closed in 1942. The company had intended that the mine be restarted, but on the death of the Earl of Lonsdale the land went to the National Trust and the constraints imposed on further working were so severe as to render profitable operation out of the question. In 1954 the company went into voluntary liquidation.

Launchy Gill Level

A magnificent example of a 16th century stope and feather working. It is about 60 ft long and situated in a dry gill below White Crags on the W side of Thirlmere (NY 312154). To reach it involves an awkward climb up the rock strewn slope immediately to the N of Rough Crag and the gill should be found some 300 ft above the road. A 12 ft rock climb is needed to reach the level mouth.

Helvellyn or Wythburn Mine

A lead mine with dressing floors at NY 325148 (900 ft. A.O.D.). These dressing floors lie immediately above the main N-S forest path and are in a totally ruined condition. The levels are higher still and anyone wishing to visit them should be prepared for quite a hard climb. The lowest level is a little to the S of the gill and lies inside the wood (1,300 ft A.O.D.): it is 600 ft long and contains no significant mineralisation. The best way to find the main cluster of levels is by following the remains of the old self-acting incline up the gill. The very large spoil heap at the top of the incline, near the drum house, belongs to No 2 level (1,750 ft A.O.D.). Above No 2 are No 1 level, Arnison's Level and Arnison's Top Level. No 3 level lies 150 ft below No 2. Coming down from No 2 is the old zig-zag miner's path which is perhaps the easiest way of getting back to the dressing floors.

Despite the size very little ore came out of the mine. It closed in 1880 when Manchester Corporation acquired the land for the Thirlmere water supply scheme.

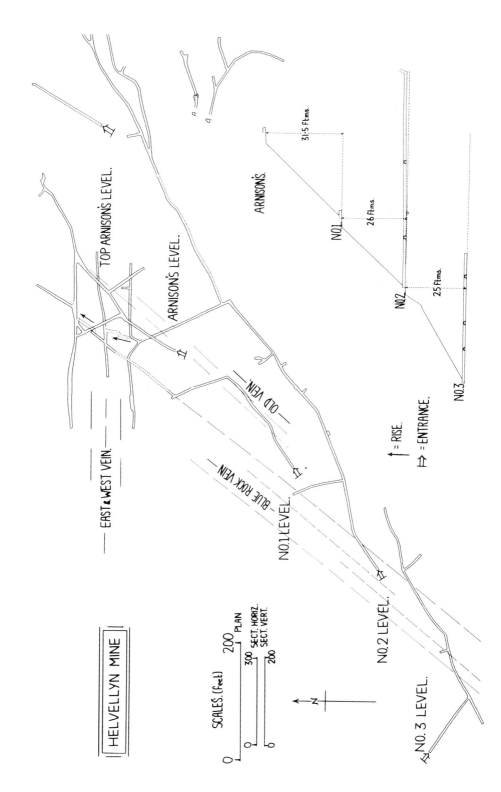

HELVELLYN MINE

SCALES. (Feet)

PLAN
200

SECT. HORIZ.
300   SECT. VERT.
200

EAST & WEST VEIN.

TOP ARNISON'S LEVEL.

ARNISON'S LEVEL.

OLD VEIN.

BLUE ROCK VEIN.

NO.1 LEVEL.

NO. 2 LEVEL.

NO. 3 LEVEL.

ARNISON'S.

N0.1.

31·5 Ftms.

26 Ftms.

N0.2.

25 Ftms.

N0.3.

↑ = RISE.

↦ = ENTRANCE.

Mining Details

Mining took place on three veins: the Blue Rock Vein, the Old Vein and the West Vein. The plan shows that a considerable amount of driving was done, most of it through barren rock. It is unlikely that enough ore was ever found to cover costs.

History

The mine was opened in 1839 by Henry Molyneux and Partners, and in 1857 the Wheal Henry Helvellyn Lead Mining Company Ltd was formed. The rest of the story is simply a succession of different companies that tried to make a go of it. The above named company was replaced in 1861 by the Wythburn Lead Mining Company, which went into liquidation in 1870; the liquidator kept the mine going until 1872 when it was purchased by the Helvellyn Mining Company. In 1873 the Cumberland Consols Mining Company took over and worked it until the final closure in 1880.

Tongue Gill Iron Mines

(Providence Mine, Fairfield Mine)

Providence Mine is to the N of Little Tongue Gill (NY 339105) and exploited two haematite bearing veins, one N-S the other NW-SE. Fairfield mine exploited a NW-SE haematite vein and is located near a reservoir at the confluence of the two Tongue Gills (NY 340098). Both mines are said to have been worked c. 1700 supplying ore to a furnace in Langdale, and official mineral statistics show them to have been active from 1873 to 1876. In the latter period Providence was worked by the Providence Iron Company Ltd (300 tons ore raised) and Fairfield by the Lake District Mining Company (204 tons ore raised).

Mines in Greenhead Gill

(Greenhead Gill Trial, Grasmere Mine)

On the N bank of Greenhead Gill, at the 600 ft contour, is a trial level some 30 ft long but showing no signs of mineralisation (NY 346085). Higher up the gill are the remains of Grasmere Lead Mine, opened in about 1564 by the company of Mines Royal and closed in 1573. The most southerly working of Grasmere Mine is a cross-cut level to the vein from the N bank of the gill at the 900 ft contour, and the most northerly workings consist of two shafts and some small openworks on the outcrop of the vein (1,000 ft contour; NY 350087).

Dunmail Raise Level

On the E side of the road between Thirlmere and Grasmere is a small copper trial (NY 333104). The level is driven E on a poor quartz vein and at about 30 ft in it turns through 90° continuing for another 30 ft or so on a southerly heading. Very little copper mineralisation is present.

Wanthwaite Crag Mine

There are several levels in the neighbourhood of NY 325225 above Lowthwaite Farm, and further trials are to be found for quite a considerable distance higher up the fell. They lie on a SW-NE system of veins which contain copper and lead ores. Some of the workings are very old but no information is available until 1850 when the sett was leased by one Henry Thompson. It was subsequently leased in 1867, 1878, 1880 and 1884 to other groups of people, the final lease being in 1887 to Mr Utrick Vipond and his short-lived Wanthwaite Crag Mining Company. The mine, though never a success, did seem to attract a good deal of interest.

Wolf Crags Level

A 30 yard long level on a poor N-S quartz vein at the foot of Wolf Crags (NY 357223). No historical details are known.

Fornside Mine

At NY 323205 on the hillside behind Fornside Farm is a 120 yard long level showing signs of copper ores. Further to the N by the diagonal path up the hillside (NY 323209) is another level which is 12 yards long and driven on a barren quartz vein.

Thirlspot Copper Mine

An old working above Thirlspot (NY 322180). There is an openwork and a spoil heap, but no sign of a level.

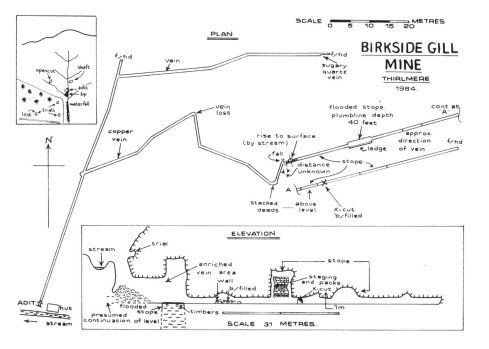

Birkside Gill Copper Mine

The main workings are clustered about NY 330126. Different sources quote different dates of working, but between 1840 and 1866 probably covers all possibilities.

Brown Cove Mine

This mine is situated at the head of Brown Cove (NY 340156) and consists of a level with a stone arched entrance which is open for about 80 yards. Nearby is a smaller trial.

Deepdale Iron Mine

A small haematite mine on the hillside above Deepdale Hall (NY 394143). It consists of two levels and a shallow openwork. The S level, which is closed, is located 200 ft immediately above Deepdale Hall and the spoil contains some fairly attractive samples of kidney ore and iron stained baryte. About 200 ft to the N is a stream and the openwork is to be found where the former emerges from a ravine. The N level can be found by climbing up the bed of the ravine and is situated some 50 yards from the openwork. The level is about 20 yards long and cuts a very poor vein.

Caiston Glen Trial

The entrance to the main level is by the side of Caiston Beck (NY 394100). It is about 26 yards long, and shows signs of galena and blende; SE of the main trial is a smaller working.

Kirkstone Pass Mine

The workings are located close to the point where Kirkstone Beck crosses under the road (NY 403093). On the W side of the road an E-W vein can be seen in the bed of the stream and by following the vein's course in a westerly direction up the hill a waterfall is reached. In front of the waterfall are some surface works and behind it is the entrance to a 40 yard long level. There is a very small working on the E side of the road – also on the course of the vein. These trials were for copper.

Swarthbeck Gill Iron Trial

A 200 yard long level situated near the foot of a waterfall in Swarthbeck Gill (NY 455206). It is well concealed and hard to find.

Dubhow Copper Mine

This small mine consists of two levels in the steep ground to the W of Angle Tarn (NY 409144). It is supposed to have been worked in 1761 and 1762. On 18th October 1850 it was leased to Messrs Jacob Craig, John Rudd and Jonathan Bainbridge. On 30th May 1862 a lease was taken by Messrs John Vipond, Parker Mandall and George Little.

Bleawick or Blowick Trial

A well concealed level by the side of a stream (NY 399176). It is about 40 yards long and follows a E-W vein which is composed almost entirely of pink stained baryte. It is reported to have been a copper trial.

Haweswater Mine

Quite a substantial group of copper workings situated at NY 495160 near the Haweswater Dam, and comprising three levels. No 2 contains a 55 ft deep shaft.

Guerness Gill Mine

A small copper mine located at the point where Guerness Gill meets the surface of Haweswater Reservoir (NY 480134). There appears to be one level only, the mouth of which is blocked with rock debris. It was worked, by persons unknown at various intervals between 1836 and 1852.

Sherry Gill Mine

A small baryte working in Sherry Gill, a little to the SW of Wet Sleddale Reservoir (NY 538104). There is a spoil heap near the foot of the gill but no obvious signs of a level. An outcrop of the vein can be seen about halfway up the gill.

Frost Hole Trials

About 200 yards to the N of Side House on the E bank of the stream are six, possibly eight, cross-cut levels driven E (SD 489986). Those still internally accessible have lengths between 20 ft and 60 ft and all were cut with the intention of finding galena.

In 1846, during the excavation of a cutting for the Kendal to Windermere railway, a lead vein was found but, as no mining was possible in the immediate area, the afore-mentioned trial was made on the assumed northern continuation of the vein. The work was financed by a Mr Robert Harrison of Hundhow, but although some strings containing a small show of argentiferous galena were found ($8\frac{1}{4}$ ozs silver per ton of lead ore) the sought after vein was not located.

Staveley Mine

A lead mine situated on the E side of the river Kent, about halfway between Staveley and Kentmere (NY 457017). It was abandoned no later than 1895.

Mining Details

Very little is known about this mine and any conclusions concerning the scale of the workings must be based on a contemporary examination of the site. The large spoil heaps outside the two main levels indicate much work having been done, though whether this was productive or mainly exploratory is difficult to judge.

The Staveley vein courses approximately NW-SE and an examination of the spoil shows galena as the main ore. Most of the work was done from two levels; the low level at NY 457017 and the high one at NY 463016. The low, driven SE on the course of the vein, is now sealed up and used as a water supply. The high level was driven S on a cross-vein, a shaft being sunk at its meeting with the main vein. The level and shaft must meet at about 60 ft below surface; the former was apparently used for the removal of material hauled up the latter. It is not known whether the high and low workings connect, but if they do the shaft could be as much as 300 ft deep.

NW and SE of the shaft, and on the course of the vein, are the remains of other levels and pits. These were probably no more than superficial trials.

History

Leases exist to show that between 1676 and 1696 various persons were prospecting in and around the Staveley Mine area. However, there is nothing to suggest any proper mining to have taken place.

In 1753 John Davies of Windsor and six partners formed a prospecting company with the aim of locating workable mineral veins on the property of the Lord of the Manor of Levens. One of the partners, Thomas Robinson, a farmer from Crosthwaite, was placed in charge of the venture and trials were made in Crosthwaite, Whitbarrow Scar and Sleddale Head, none of which proved successful. Then in 1755 the lead vein at Staveley was found. Under the direction of Antony Houghton, a miner from Davies' Staffordshire mines, a shaft was sunk on the bank of the river but problems with flooding caused this work to be abandoned; instead the low level was started. The high workings are also supposed to have been initiated by this company. Davies was evidently pleased with the mine for in 1776 he renewed his lease for another 21 years.

Between 1812 and 1826 the lease was held by Geo. Sayer of The Heights, Hugill. Some time between the end of this lease and the commencement of another in 1865 the mine was worked by 16 to 20 Cornish miners employed by John Barratt of Coniston Mines.

In 1865 the mine was leased by Nathaniel Caine of Broughton. Presumably by this time the Staveley vein was no longer considered worth working for Caine is reported to have been looking for other veins on the property. In September 1867 he found one which turned out to be worthless, and by November 1870 the venture was abandoned. Between 1870 and 1895 the mine was held by Walter Eddy of Llangollen and James Nancarron of Liverpool. Nothing else is known for this period.

Pool Scar Trial

On Pool Scar, a little to the S of Staveley Mine and about 60 ft above the road, is a 30 ft long trial level (NY 459008). It cuts a very thin quartz vein but is devoid of ore minerals.

Borwick Fold Mine

A small lead mine at Borwick Fold (SD 442969). Two veins, one ENE and the other NNW, cross here and a shaft, reported to be 126 ft deep, was sunk at their intersection. There was once an engine at the top of the shaft and the scant remains of the engine-house can still be found. The pond to the E was created, or enlarged, by the construction of a dam which provided a water supply for the mine.

Knipe Tarn Mine

About 400 yards to the SW of Knipe Tarn is an E-W vein containing baryte and a small quantity of galena (SD 423942). It is reported that a level was driven into the hill and connected with a 60 ft deep shaft sunk from the surface. There is now no trace of either but over the wall, on the N side of the road, can be seen a rubbish-filled openwork.

Whitbarrow Scar Trial

A short distance to the E of Pool Bank and on Whitbarrow Scar is a short trial level (SD 436877). It was probably driven c. 1753 by John Davies and Company (see Staveley Mine).

Red Tarn Mine

In 1860 a Mr Crain made some test borings and shallow pits along a northerly line extending 300 yards from the N end of Red Tarn (NY 268038), his purpose being to try a N-S iron vein. The property was subsequently held from 1872 to 1875 by Thomas Massicks and Company.

Coniston United Mine

Not to be confused with Coniston Copper Mines, this small group of trials consists of two levels (NY 354019, 358021) and a shaft (NY 347021) located near Pull Beck S of Skelwith Bridge. The shaft is sunk on a NNE-SSW fault and nothing is known of its depth or the workings at its foot. The levels are both about 100 yards long and show little mineralisation. The mine was being worked *c*. 1853.

Cockley Beck Mines

Two small copper mines are to be found in the neighbourhood of Cockley Beck. On the N side of the beck is a very old working (NY 249013) consisting of one, possibly two, level(s) and a shaft. Nearby is a ruin and on its floor can be found many small pieces of malachite. The only information to have been found on this mine was that it was being worked *c*. 1700. The mine to the S of the beck (NY 247013) consists of a shaft and associated haulage level and is probably of 19th century origin.

Much further S, above Dale Head (NY 245005), is a very short (12 ft) and quite barren level, and S of this is another level (closed) at NY 244001.

Dunnerdale Mine

An iron mine on the hillside above Carter Ground (SD 228924). There are several collapsed levels, a shaft and a flattened area which was probably the site of dressing operations. The mine is known to have been worked from 1872 to 1874. The proprietor was the Carnforth Iron Company and a total of 6,555 tons of ore was raised.

Mines of the Coniston Fells

A considerable amount of mining activity has taken place on the fells adjacent to Coniston, and a full description of all the workings would itself be of book length. Such a book has already been written by Eric Holland, *Coniston Copper Mines: a Field Guide* published by Cicerone Press, Milnthorpe, Cumbria. The following is a brief account of the major workings.

Coniston Copper Mines

The workings occupy a belt of land extending from the head of Coppermines valley (SD 290985) to Levers Water (SD 280993). They were at their most productive in the 1850s but thereafter, as a result of intense foreign competition, went steadily into decline, closing in 1915. Some short-lived prospecting work was done in 1954.

Mining Details

The mine exploited a complex system of E-W to SE-NW veins and reference to the plan will show just how elaborate and extensive the workings were. The principal lodes are the Paddy End Old Vein, New South Vein, South Vein, Belman Hole Vein, Kernal Vein, Park's Vein, Triddle Vein, Bonser Vein and the South Lode, but there are others. The Bonser Vein was the most important, and was almost wholly stoped out to a depth of 205 fathoms below the Deep Level, or 255 fathoms below surface. The Paddy End part of the mine ranked second.

Output in the 1850s was of the order of 3,000 tons of ore per annum, but from 1860 onwards steadily declined to a value of 1,000 tons in 1876. Thereafter production was relatively small and never, after 1884, exceeded 200 tons per annum. Copper pyrite was the main ore, though in 1855 three tons of nickel and cobalt ore were raised, and in 1893 12 tons of lead ore.

History

Though supposedly wrought by the Romans, documentary evidence of working is not available prior to that for the 16th century. From about 1590 it was worked under the auspices of the Elizabethan company of Mines Royal, and the mine is known to have been active until at least 1620. Why it should have taken Mines Royal so long to discover the rich veins at Coniston is something of a puzzle.

The next record, dated 25th May 1686, is a letter written from John Blackwell to the landowner Sir Daniel Fleming, stating that he (Blackwell) has examined the ground and is prepared to re-open the mines if mutually acceptable royalty fees can be agreed. Further proposals were made in 1691, but there is no evidence to indicate that work actually took place.

Sometime around the 1760s a Macclesfield-based company commenced mining under the direction of one of their partners, Charles Roe, and surviving accounts for between 1767 and 1775 show 904 tons of ore to have been raised in the eight-year period. The year of abandonment is not known, but was almost certainly prior to 1800.

In 1824 the mine was leased by John Taylor who appointed John Barratt (b. 1794-d. 1866) manager. In 1834 the lease was in the name of Taylor and Barratt. Taylor subsequently withdrew, but Barratt continued right up to his death: his son, Joseph, then took over. However, the declining prosperity of the mine resulted in it being put up for sale on 3rd August 1875 (along with Tilberthwaite Mine). Purchased by a Thomas Wynn, for £3,000, the continuing decline caused it once again to be sold, this time to one Charles Edwin Day. Very little work was done; Day lost all his money and in 1908 the mine closed.

In 1912 a French-owned company, Coniston Electrolytic Copper Company

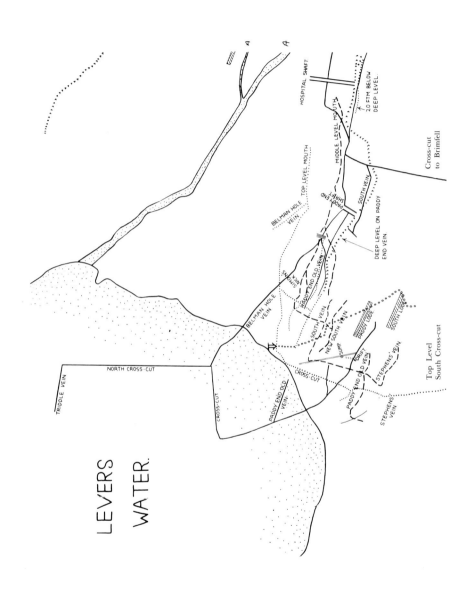

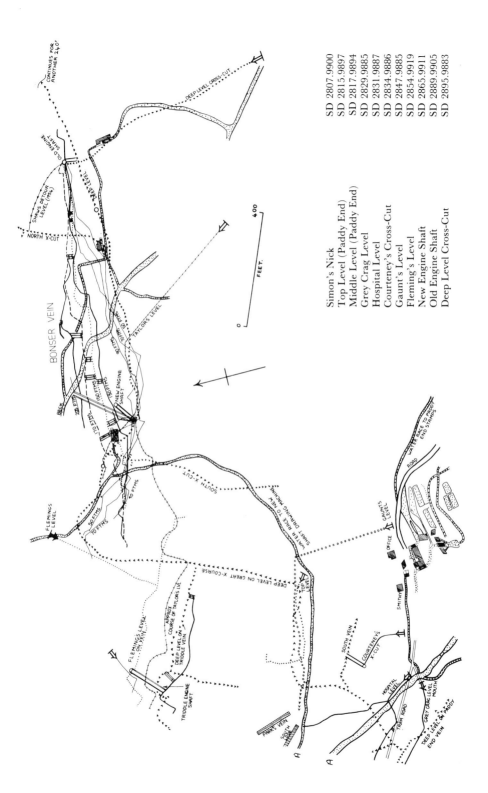

SD 2807.9900
SD 2815.9897
SD 2817.9894
SD 2829.9885
SD 2831.9887
SD 2834.9886
SD 2847.9885
SD 2854.9919
SD 2865.9911
SD 2889.9905
SD 2895.9883

Simon's Nick
Top Level (Paddy End)
Middle Level (Paddy End)
Grey Crag Level
Hospital Level
Courteney's Cross-Cut
Gaunt's Level
Fleming's Level
New Engine Shaft
Old Engine Shaft
Deep Level Cross-Cut

Ltd, leased the mine with the intention of testing a patent process to extract copper from the dumps by flotation, followed by electrolysis. The company never did any mining, except to obtain samples for testing the process, and the scheme was a commercial failure. The mine manager, Mr J. J. Calderwood, declared himself able to recoup the losses if the company would agree to his working the mine in a conventional manner but it would not entertain the idea. Work stopped in 1915 following the loss of £12,000.

In 1954 W. T. Shaw, on behalf of McKechnie Brothers (see Force Crag, Hartsop Hall and the Caldbeck Fells Barytes Mines), set out to examine the bottom of the stopes on the Paddy End Vein, but direct attempts to access the old workings failed owing to their dangerous condition. An effort was then made to access the workings via the Deep Level of Bonser Mine, and a 300 ft detour level was cut to get round the collapsed workings near the Engine Shaft, but on returning to the Deep Level further collapses were found, and it was not considered worthwhile to continue.

Seathwaite Tarn Mine

A copper mine consisting of three widely separated levels which are to be found over a half mile length of Tarn Head Beck (low level SD 261993). The mine's sole claim to fame is as the hiding place of Rowf and Snitter, the fugitive dogs, in Richard Adams' novel *The Plague Dogs*.

The low level is about 200 yards long and follows a meandering course in a northerly direction. The first 15 yards is stone arched and although the level portal collapsed a good many years ago the rest of the arching is intact, albeit in a dangerous condition. The level contains no stopes or cross-cuts and appears devoid of mineralisation. The middle level, further upstream, is closed but the spoil shows a reasonable presence of copper minerals. Nearby are the remains of dressing floors and mine buildings. The top level is open, about 400 yards long, and like the low level follows a northerly course without stopes, cross-cuts or mineralisation. A few yards downstream from the spoil of the top level, on the opposite side of the beck, are the overgrown remains of what is very probably another level.

The only historical information to have been found is that in September 1860 John Barratt of Coniston Mine forfeited his lease of the mine for not having worked it with sufficient regularity.

Tilberthwaite Mine

An ancient copper mine occupying an 800 ft broad belt of land between the waterfall at the head of Tilberthwaite Gill (NY 299008) and a SW-NE line of workings near the old mine road at NY 299010. The last work was in 1942.

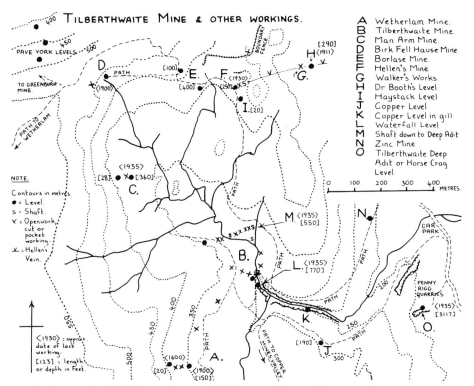

Based upon the 1974 Ordnance Survey 1:10,000 map with permission of the Controller of Her Majesty's Stationery Office, Crown Copyright reserved.

Mining Details

The mine exploited a system of seven E-W to ENE-WSW veins. From N to S the five named ones are the North Lode, Shaft Lode, Benson's Lode, Benson's South Lode and Spedding's Lode.

There are numerous relatively minor workings on the backs of the veins but the major work was done from the Waterfall Level and the Deep Adit, 145 ft and 550 ft below surface respectively. Both levels were driven to intersect all the lodes in depth. The Waterfall Level entrance is near the foot of the waterfall at the head of Tilberthwaite Gill (NY 299008), and the entrance to the Deep Adit is in Horse Crag Quarry (NY 30550070). The Deep Adit, 1,039 yards in length, was driven by John Barratt in about 1850. About 80 yards in from its entrance is a sizeable subterranean slate working or closehead.

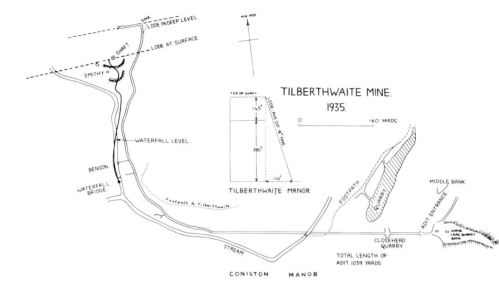

History

The mine was worked by the Elizabethans in the late 16th and early 17th centuries, and various fragmentary records show it also to have been worked in the 18th century.

From the 1850s – possibly earlier – until 1908, it was held by the owners of Coniston Copper Mines, the Barratt family (1850-1875); Thomas Wynn (1875-1894); and Charles Day (1894-1908). In 1912-1913 the mine was owned by the Central Chile Copper Company Ltd, and in 1917 by the Langdale Silver Lead and Copper Company Ltd.

The final tenant was the Greenburn and Tilberthwaite Mining Company of London who, in about 1930, cleaned out the Deep Adit and put a ladder way through to surface. Nothing of value was found and in 1942 the company was in liquidation. None of the proprietors appear to have done particularly well out of the mine.

Greenburn or New Coniston or Great Coniston Mine

A copper mine whose main workings are located at NY 290022 on the S bank of Greenburn Beck. Further S in steep ground are the Pave York and

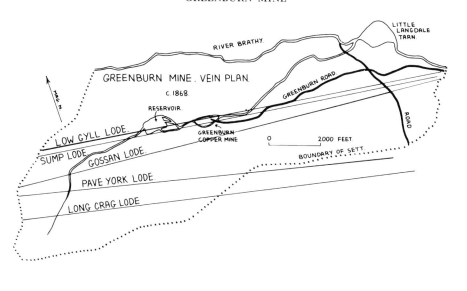

GREENBURN MINE. VEIN PLAN.

c. 1868.

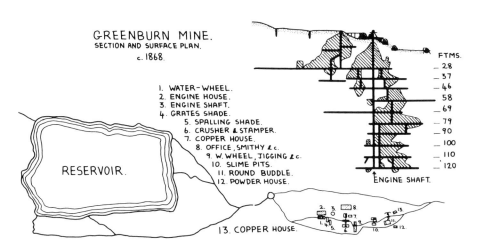

GREENBURN MINE.
SECTION AND SURFACE PLAN.
c. 1868.

1. WATER-WHEEL.
2. ENGINE HOUSE.
3. ENGINE SHAFT.
4. GRATES SHADE.
5. SPALLING SHADE.
6. CRUSHER & STAMPER.
7. COPPER HOUSE.
8. OFFICE, SMITHY &c.
9. W. WHEEL, JIGGING &c.
10. SLIME PITS.
11. ROUND BUDDLE.
12. POWDER HOUSE.
13. COPPER HOUSE.

Long Crag workings. These are part of the sett; the former are in the neighbourhood of NY 291017 and the latter NY 286015. The period of prosperous working was prior to 1865 and little appears to have been done since.

Mining Details

There are five named E-W veins traversing the sett and all have been worked to varying degrees; N to S they are the Low Gill Lode, Sump Lode, Gossan Lode, Pave York Lode and Long Crag Lode. A brief description of the work done on all the lodes is given in a report by Captain S. Vivian, dated 7th December 1865. It states:

> The class of ore are the yellow sulphurets of copper, yielding from 10 per cent to 20 per cent of fine copper. Considerable quantities of such ores were raised from the Sump Lode, on which a shaft has been sunk 120 fathoms deep, the ore lasting all the depth from near the surface. These workings have yielded about £14,000 worth of ore.
>
> A shaft has been sunk on the Gossan Lode, which is about 55 fathoms south of the Sump Lode, about 5 fathoms deep, which is said to have a branch of ore in it six inches wide. Said lode is 3 ft in width, of a most promising character, but the shaft was suspended in consequence of having so much water. An adit level is being driven, which will come in about 7 fathoms deeper than said shaft in about two months hence.
>
> The next, 204 fathoms south, is the Pave York Lode, which is 12 ft wide, and has yielded several tons of ore near the surface. For the small amount of work done on it, I consider this to be the main lode, and is deserving of vigorous prosecution.
>
> The next is Long Crag Lode, $3\frac{1}{2}$ ft in width, about 120 fathoms south of Pave York, which has also yielded several tons of ore near the surface; but being so far up the mountain, and no road to it, was abandoned.
>
> The next is Low Gill Lode 3 ft in width, and about 45 fathoms north of the Sump Lode. Nothing has been done more than to prove its existence, and that it produced specimens of ore.

History

The mine, relatively speaking, is probably not all that old and a starting date *c.* 1845 is suggested. Up to the 1860s it was worked successfully by Messrs Crossfield and others, but in 1864 the lease was renewed, for 21 years, by a merchant called David Dunlop. Thereafter things become rather confusing, for under Dunlop's lease several companies were formed but it is not known which worked the mine, or which were still-born for want of shareholders. In about 1868 there appeared the New Coniston Copper Mining Company; in 1872 the Langdale Mining Company; in 1873 the Great Coniston Mining Company, also the Greenburn Copper Mining Company; and in 1875 McGowan and Cooper. The next record of tenancy is the Greenburn and Tilberthwaite Syndicate from 1906 to 1911, and the Langdale Silver Lead and Copper Company from 1912 to 1917. One of these later companies did a little work at Pave York.

Index

The four-figure grid references given below are for use with the map on page 156. Where greater accuracy is required the reader should refer to an appropriate O.S. map and the references quoted within the text.

Wherever possible a mine has been called by its historically correct name. In cases where this is not known the name now commonly used has been adopted.

The regions A to F are the creation of the author and serve only as convenient partitions of a rather large area.

A.   Thornthwaite Forest, Derwent Fells, Borrowdale Fells

MAP SHOWING MINES AND MINING AREAS (O.S. GRID SYSTEM.

B. Skiddaw, Caldbeck Fells

C.   Ennerdale and Buttermere

D.   Eskdale and the Fells south of Eskdale

E.   East of Thirlmere and Windermere

F.   Coniston Area